THE BOOK OF ANIMALS

COMMON LEOPARD.

THE
BOOK OF ANIMALS

An Album of Natural History

WRITTEN BY

HORACE G. GROSER

AUTHOR OF

"OUT WITH THE OLD VOYAGERS" ETC.

WITH COLOURED PLATES PREPARED FROM SPECIAL
PAINTINGS BY A. SCOTT RANKIN, AND NUMEROUS
BLACK AND WHITE ILLUSTRATIONS BY JOSEPH
WOLF, STANLEY L. WOOD, A. T. ELWES, FREDERICK
BURTON, GEORGE RANKIN, COLBRON PEARSE, ETC.

LONDON:
ANDREW MELROSE
16 PILGRIM STREET, E.C.
1906

TO

OSWALD VERNON GROSER

AND HIS COUSIN

ARTHUR GEOFFREY GROSER

CONTENTS

LIST OF ILLUSTRATIONS

COLOURED PLATES

THE BOOK OF ANIMALS

THE TIGER.

TIGER IN OPEN-AIR CAGE AT THE ZOOLOGICAL GARDENS.

SPLENDID in his strength and quickness, the Tiger moves through the hot forests of Asia like some fierce robber-king, the terror of every village he approaches. His name has become a byword for ferocious courage. If he be teased, he snarls. If he be roused, he is up in a moment, ready for the

I

lightning leap. And if he does leap, teeth and claws soon do their dreadful work.

India is his chief home, and he is not found outside Asia. But his range is very wide indeed. Among the dry, long grass of the Indian jungle and the dense Malayan forests, sportsmen go out to shoot him. Yet he is also found far northward among the Himalayas, the chain of mountains, high and snow-crowned, which are India's northern wall. In Burmah he is such a pest that in the year 1905 the Government offered £1, 10s. for every cub killed, and twice that sum for a full-grown specimen. And in Manchuria, where Russians and Japanese fought so long and stubbornly, and where the winters are bitterly cold, a particularly large and fine species is to be met with. Even Siberia has its Tiger, two specimens of which arrived at the London Zoo, in July 1906.

Perhaps no beast of prey is quite so graceful and beautiful as the Tiger. With its bright tawny coat of thick fur, banded and striped with black, and fading into white underneath the body, it is a most striking-looking creature. Even the leopard is not so beautiful. When it springs, or when, being startled, it throws up its head, it is a grand beast ; yet when stealthily and noiselessly it creeps towards its prey, it is as lithe and easy in its movements as a sleek cat stalking the garden sparrows.

Woe to the poor child or gentle deer that is not watchful, if a Tiger means to carry it off. There may be no sound of footsteps, nor crackle of dead leaves, nor snapping of twigs, only perhaps the unnoticed movement of the dry grass which there is no wind to stir. Then suddenly a long, lean, striped body shoots forward—out of the ground as it seems—and the next minute the child or the deer is gone, and a quick rustling in the tall grass tells where the Tiger is making for his den.

A Tiger does not like the open country, and he hates to have to come out into it, unless he be a man-eater ; in which case he will dare almost anything. By nature he is a forest dweller. The tall, dry grass of the plains will do, but he prefers to have an impenetrable thicket of shrubs and trees to fly to for better safety.

Look at a Tiger as he stands or lies in his cage at the Zoo. His beauty of colouring would seem to make him a noticeable figure wherever he might go. But in his Indian home, those stripes against the almost orange fur are just the very best concealment for him—so strangely do those markings resemble the

THE TIGER KING.

[*Drawn by* GEORGE RANKIN.

jungle grass through which he loves to creep and prowl. (This, by the bye, is an example of what scientists call " protective mimicry "—a phrase which even my younger readers will be able to pick to pieces and guess the meaning of.)

A poet who wrote lovely little poems for children, William Blake, begins one of them thus :

"Tiger, Tiger, burning bright,
In the forests of the night,"

and such words seem to bring the creature before us, with its rich warm colouring and flashing eyes and gleaming teeth. Many of you have seen Tiger skins laid down in houses as rugs or mats, but these give you very little idea of the grand appear-

JUNO, A TIGER CUB FOUR MONTHS OLD.

ance of the living animal. Its size, however, can be guessed, for the best of such skins usually measure about eleven and a half feet long. The thick-furred Tigers of Northern Asia are the largest of all ; the skin of one of them, brought home to Europe, actually measured thirteen and a half feet from nose to tip of tail !

A Tiger, like other members of the cat-tribe large and small, loves to stalk his prey. Having sighted it he will crawl after it for long distances, using every bit of cover,—bushes, trees, long grass,—just like a modern soldier advancing to the attack. He has an odd habit of making himself as small as he can, by drawing in his breath and flattening his fur, when he thinks he is likely to be detected. And thus an untrained eye would probably not be able to see him though he might be fast approaching.

Fiercely bold though he is, he will not go out of his way to fight for a meal. He knows the dark men-creatures often carry knives that slash and hurt, and the white men-creatures go about with fire-darting tubes, and he prefers to give them the go-by. So he interferes as little as possible with the armed native and the European with the rifle, and he devotes his attention to the defenceless woman, or the unsuspecting child. They give him less trouble.

TIGER CUB, RESTING AFTER EXERCISE.

(Notice the already huge paws.)

At some convenient place, where he can see without being seen, he lies in wait. A road along which persons are sure to pass, but not too many of them ; the banks of a *nullah* (ravine, with a stream running along the bed of it), at the part where there is a favourite crossing ; or the dark shade of a korinda bush, with its drooping, thickly leaved branches,—such are the likeliest spots where a Tiger may be found lurking.

When he springs he strikes his victim with his forepaws. Few creatures but go down under such a blow. For the feet of a Tiger are huge, and they strike like a heavy mallet. But, as if that was not enough, they are armed with talons that rend and tear in the most terrible fashion.

It is said that there is something peculiarly deadly about the wound given by a Tiger's claws. It causes lockjaw, and death soon follows.

Of course, when the fearful teeth are also used, any one may imagine what little chance his victim has either of recovery or of escape.

It is not only deer and such timid creatures that a Tiger will pounce upon. He will attack the Indian buffalo, which is the very picture of solid strength.

One of these patient broad-backed beasts, that draw the peasant's plough and carry his loads, once got stuck in a quag-mire (buffaloes love wallowing in mud and water). His master, unable to haul the animal out, went off for help. When he and his neighbours hurried to the spot, the great beast had been dragged out already—by a Tiger! He had pulled the buffalo out and killed it, and sucked all the blood from its body. Holding his huge burden in his teeth, he had tossed it over his shoulder, and was just about to trot off to his den, when the party of natives came running up. At once he dropped his prey and bolted.

But think of the enormous strength needed to treat like that a great ox-like animal weighing over 1000 lbs.—more than double his own weight.

To watch a Tiger steadily and greedily making a meal of some large animal he has killed is a horrid sight. He gorges himself upon it, and then lies quiet for three days, dozing and blinking in the hot sunshine, and waiting till he has appetite enough for another meal. He is not a very clean feeder, and rather than miss any part of an animal killed and left half-eaten, he will return and finish it when it has " gone bad."

One thing a Tiger *must* have when he is dining : that is water to quench his feverish thirst. So he takes care to strike down his prey within fairly easy distance of a pool or running stream.

THE MAN-EATER'S LAST SPRING.

[*Drawn by* STANLEY L. WOOD.

You may ask, What do the people of the country do to rid themselves of such a terrible pest?

In some cases they do nothing, trusting that if they let the fierce animal alone he will let them alone, and be content with a four-footed victim. Not so long ago, the rajahs, or native rulers, used to issue orders that no one was to kill a Tiger. They wished to have the pleasure of hunting him—some day, when they had a mind to. Meanwhile, if he injured any one, or stole the poor man's sheep or goat, well! it could not be helped. The sufferers must wait the king's pleasure.

Then, at last, the great day would come. The well-trained elephants, perhaps to the number of twenty or thirty, are brought out, each carrying its *mahout* or native driver seated astride its broad neck, and bearing on its back the *howdah*, in which is room for two or more huntsmen to sit. Horsemen, and dogs, and native servants make up the party.[1] Then away they go into the long grass of the jungle, everybody keenly eager to get sight of the lurking Tiger.

Presently, one of the mahouts from his high seat espies a long, striped body making off through the grass and bushes, and gives the alarm. Then the excitement is greater than ever. The dogs bark, the natives shout and yell, and the sportsmen of the party, very likely including one or two British guests of the rajah, hold their rifles ready to shoot.

The Tiger is driven from cover to cover. By this time, the hunters seem all round him. He can see no way of escape. What shall he do? He is a clever beast, and a cunning one; but no cunning will avail him now. He cowers in the grass, thinking. Then, swift as an arrow, he flies straight at the nearest elephant.

His great claws are driven into the thick hide, but he loses his hold and falls sprawling. Before he can spring to his feet, an older elephant rushes forward. It is a she elephant, and therefore without tusks. But her great foot is stretched out, pinning the Tiger to the ground. Then with a jerk that nearly unseats the scolding mahout, and makes the sportsman clutch the edge of

---

[1] Sometimes as many as a hundred elephants have been used at a hunt, and the babel of tongues chattering and shouting, as the great beasts are being got ready, is a strange contrast to the orderly start of an English hunting party.

the howdah, she drops upon the snarling beast, crushing the life out of him with her huge knees.

So dies the first Tiger. But others are not far off, and the next falls to the rajah's gun, the other sportsmen purposely not firing, so that he may have the honour of " a kill."

Nowadays, there are many ways of killing a Tiger. One of the favourite plans is this. A platform or scaffold is built in the jungle, raised upon four stout bamboo poles, say 20 feet high, driven securely into the ground. The sportsman, alone or with his native servant, climbs to the platform and crouches waiting. It may be late, or it may be soon, but at last, if they have made their plans wisely, the Tiger appears. He sniffs the air and comes forward. For the hunters have placed a dead ox (or, more cruelly, a live one, tied to a tree) just where he is likely to pass. He pounces on the bait, and finds, too late, that it is a trap, or rather, a decoy. The rifle-shots ring out in quick succession, and " Stripes " rolls over—dead.

Sometimes the bullets go wide, and the Tiger springs up at the hunter's perch. But the smooth, hard bamboo poles give no chance even to *his* sharp claws, and he falls back snarling.

I heard, about a year or two ago, of an exciting adventure which befell a sportsman perched on one of these jungle platforms. Darkness had closed in, and he was getting tired of waiting, when suddenly, right beneath him, he saw two gleaming eyes looking up. Snatching up his rifle, he was pointing it at the Tiger, when to his horror the platform gave a lurch, and began slowly to give way. He fell to the ground, striking his head, and knew no more till he found himself in a bungalow (house) with his friends watching beside him.

It appeared that his bamboo platform had been built on soft ground, and had sunk in the mud. He had been thrown out, almost into the Tiger's jaws. But the moon just then rose above the tree-tops, and by its light his friend, watching from a platform close by, had fired, and shot the creature dead.

When a Tiger has once tasted human blood he thinks little of other food. Henceforth he is a man-eater. Great, then, is the terror that he excites. He becomes daring. He will carry off man, woman, or child, even under the eyes of the victim's friends. One Tigress in the Nilgiri Hills, is known to have killed two hundred persons!

No wonder, then, that the British *sahib* (master) who can shoot straight, is a welcome visitor to a Tiger-haunted neighbourhood. Great is the gratitude of the poor natives when they are shown the skin of the robber.

Let me close with a story that shows this savage brute in a pleasanter light. A famous animal tamer relates it.

"Once a very fierce old Tigress which we had in London had nearly killed my brother, and her keepers were afraid of her. It happened that she ran a bit of bone into her paw, and it made her miserable. I promised to take out the splinter."

This is how he did it. Ropes were thrown over the Tigress, and she was drawn close up to the bars, and held there by four men. At first she struggled and growled fiercely. Then suddenly it seemed as if she guessed why she was being held and hurt, and she stopped growling, and permitted the trainer to cut the splinter out.

The next day she allowed him to put a poultice on the paw, and up to the day of her death she would let him enter her cage whenever he wished.

Who will say, after this, that a Tiger cannot feel gratitude?

THE END OF THE TIGER HUNT.

THE OTTER.

THE Otter is one of the few remaining "wild beasts" that once upon a time lived and fed, played and fought, in Old England. He and the badger and the fox still remain; the wild cat, the beaver, the wild boar, and the wolf are gone.

To the sportsman who comes down to the riverside to fish, and to the keeper who gets the blame if there are no fine fish to be caught, the Otter is an enemy, a bold pirate, a destructive little miscreant who does thrice as much damage as he need do, even to keep himself well fed.

For, say they, the Otter goes after the best fish. He kills his prey, and ought to be satisfied with it. But he is a most dainty feeder; he will eat just the parts which he likes best, and, wastefully leaving the rest, he will go and kill sometimes as many as three more fish that day.

But those who love all wild creatures, and think that each has a right to his share of river or forest, and the good things therein, admire the Otter very much. He is shy, but if hard pressed he will turn pluckily and fight to the death. He is equally at home on land and in water. He will dive from the bank like a flash, and, swimming with great speed under water, will come up to breathe quite a long distance down the stream. As for the mother Otter, besides being plucky like her mate, and wonderfully agile, she is full of love for her children, and will play with them in the prettiest way imaginable.

Let us see what the Otter is like. He is a long, slim creature in a coat of brown, sleek fur, with an outer coat of long, coarse hair. Measured, tail and all—his tail is about fourteen inches—he is usually between 3 and 3½ feet in length. His sharp-clawed toes are webbed, and this helps him to swim fast. His tail is as good as a rudder, and in the river-current he uses it as such. His wits are sharp, so is his sense of hearing, but sharpest of all are his white teeth.   And as he has so much to do with slippery fish and wriggling eels that fact is very important.

He will honour any good lake or pool with his presence, if there is plenty to eat there ; but he loves running water best, and a riverside dweller is what he prefers to be.

He will dig a burrow for his home if need be, but more often he takes possession of some hole or cleft already made, and conveniently near the water.   This is soon turned into a comfortable home for the baby Otters-to-be, by means of a warm, dry lining of leaves and reeds.

The babies appear about March or April, and very early become good swimmers too.   But just at first they are scared, like many a little boy or girl bathing for the first time.   Often the mother Otter has to drop her cub into the water, and let him find out the way to float and paddle himself along.   Then she leans down, and, picking him out, lands him safely, and gives him a small eel or tiny fish to eat.

Very often she teaches him just in the same way that your big brother may have taught you.   She makes him get on her back, and then plunges into the water.   She dives, and he tries to keep up.   Then while he is spluttering and panting, she swims back, and helps him to reach the shore.

The Otter loves quiet.   For that reason, if he cannot get a stream that is peaceful and lonely, he will find out the quiet places in it.   On such a river as the Thames, a favourite choice would be the thick osier beds, where willows and reeds and water-plants grow in a glorious jungle, and a human foot scarcely ever intrudes.   Here he can lie snugly hid, here he can eat the fish he has brought ashore ; and where there are sun-warmed, open spaces behind the wall of tall reeds he curls himself up and *basks.* Yet he is a hardy little fellow, as becomes so bold a freebooter. His stream or pool may be icy cold, half-frozen indeed, but he cares not a whit.

A writer in the *Spectator* tells of what he noticed one day in the winter of 1895.   He says : "On the Saturday on which the great frost began, the Otter at the Zoo had just been provided with warm, dry straw to make its bed.   Part of it had been pushed into his house, while some lay on the little bridge over his pond.   All the Otter had to do was to step out of his house on to the bridge and pull the dry straw in.

"But with Otters it is the rule to do no work on dry ground which can possibly be done in the water." [Often a very good rule, as anything heavy, for instance, can more easily be towed by water than dragged or carried overland.]

So, instead of pulling the straw in dry, he brought it all through the water, and drew it dripping into his bed.   Then he prepared to go to sleep on it.   And this, says the writer, "on the coldest night of the year!"

Otter hunting is still kept up in England and elsewhere, and great is the excitement when the Otter hounds see him, a slim dark form, swimming for his life.

In a moment the smooth surface of the stream is full of bobbing heads, all going in pursuit.   Sometimes he will run up the bank and turn at

OTTER BELOW A WATERFALL.

bay. Then he sells his life dearly, and his sharp teeth often send back the foremost of his foes limping and whining.

There are Otters as far west as Cornwall, and as far north as the Shetlands and the Hebrides, but in those treeless isles rocks and stones have to give the shelter which reeds and leaves afford in the south.

But the Otter is found in many other parts of the world. In India and China it is caught young, and trained to catch fish for its master. This is quite an old custom. Good Bishop Heber tells how, when he was at Pondicherry, he saw a row of nearly a dozen fine, large Otters by the riverside, all ready. They were "chained" to bamboo stakes by means of long strings and straw collars. Some were rolling lazily on the hot sand, some were swimming about as far as their tether allowed, some lay half in, half out of the water.

He learned that most of the fishermen in the place kept one or more of these sleek, lithe creatures, which were almost as tame as dogs. They would either bring fish ashore in their sharp teeth, or drive a shoal of them into nets spread ready.

. Otters have been thus trained, in several cases, in this country. Years ago, an Inverness gentleman bought an Otter cub, and taught it to answer to its name, and follow him about like a dog. It grew up quite devoted to him. When taken to the waterside it would hunt, and bring in as many as eight or ten salmon a day. When tired it " struck " work. Then it was given a good meal. After that it lay down, curled itself up, and went to sleep ; and so was taken up and carried home.

A larger member of the Otter family is found on the western coast of North America. This is the famous Kalan or Sea Otter. Its size is twice that of its European cousin, and its black-and-brown fur is so wonderfully beautiful that a single skin is worth sometimes as much as a hundred pounds.

The Sea Otter would long ago have been " killed out " by hunters and trappers anxious to make money, were it not that the hunting of those that remain is very difficult and dangerous.

His relatives once lived happily enough on the more southern coasts—as far south, indeed, as California. But man came and killed them all. Now, if he would catch the shy creature, he has to go right up into that dreary region called Alaska, where the waves roll in upon shores and rocky islets often sheathed in ice and snow.

The Alaskan native knows he can get much money for even one skin, and he dares a great deal to obtain it.

Like his forefathers he goes out, warmly clad in furs, and paddles along the coast in his *bidarka*, which is pretty much like an Eskimo's *kayak*. And even should he be so lucky as to see an Otter, it is ten chances to one whether he catches it. Danger has made the poor Otter watchfulness itself. Even the smell of a distant camp-fire will scare him away from a favourite resort.

Only the most hardy, skilful, and plucky Alaskan natives hunt the Sea Otter, and a long training is needful before a young hunter is allowed to join an Otter-hunting party.

Harpoons and spears used to be the weapons, but now fire-arms have largely taken the place of the old-fashioned bone-tipped darts. No wonder the Sea Otter is gradually disappearing from off the face of the earth.

> " A hunted thing, he dreads the shore,
>   And shuns the haunts of men,
> From Attu to the Chernaboor
>   He dwells without their ken :
> He harbours where no harbours are,
>   Upon the ocean's breast,
> On seaward rafts of weed afar
>   He snatches troubled rest."

But when the winter storms rush and scream over those waters he flees before them. He comes ashore. Then the hunter has his chance—and takes it. And another lovely fur is sold in London, or Paris, or New York.

THE IBEX.

HE belongs to a very big clan—that of the wild goats—and he is a very distinguished member of that clan. He has all the agility and sure-footedness of the chamois, but he is a sturdier, stronger animal. His length is usually about three feet, and his height about forty inches at the shoulder.

Ibexes move about in little companies, and seem to obey their leader like well-disciplined soldiers. His shrill cry of alarm—a sort of sharp whistle—is instantly heard and obeyed by them. If they are on a slope it is usual for them to turn and make for the highest and most hard-to-reach places among the dizzy crags.

The eyes of an Ibex, except when it is angered, are almost as soft and beautiful as those of a gazelle, but its nature is very different. It is a bold, independent, freedom-loving creature.

Look at its horns—huge for its size. It used to be said that when it needed to take a flying leap from a great height on to the rocks below it would so jump as to alight on its horns, and thus break the force of the fall. And whether that is fact or fable, it is quite in keeping with the character of this fearless mountaineer.

The Ibex was once not uncommon in the Alps, but for many years past the number has been quite small, even if they can still be said to exist in a wild state. The people who have to live in those mountain districts have no great wish for more of them.

King Victor Emmanuel of Italy, grieved to hear how scarce the Swiss Ibexes were becoming, collected a herd, and had them driven into one of the rich valleys (the Vale of Aosta). Here they throve wonderfully, and their numbers increased, but they became quite a nuisance and a terror to the country people. For they lost their shyness, and became so bold and quarrelsome that they would rush at passers-by, butting at them like angry goats.

This was no laughing matter. For an Ibex is all bone and

2

sinew, and when it is in a rage its great strength is dangerous even to a strong man, unless he be armed.

A Swiss gentleman was walking with his wife and little girl along the road from Coire, one September day, when a splendid Ibex suddenly stepped out from a bend in the road, and began to follow them.

Something had roused the animal's ill-temper. Presently it lowered its head and rushed at the gentleman. He stepped aside and caught hold of it by the horns, but was dragged hither and thither and thrown to the ground. He managed to scramble to his feet, but the enraged beast knocked him down again, and rolled with him to the foot of the steep slope.

The poor traveller hung on to the great curved horns, but the Ibex pulled him about from side to side of the pathway, trying to free itself. He would probably have been stunned and killed by the furious creature, had not a shepherd come running up. With his long knife he struck the Ibex again and again in the neck, till it beat a retreat, seemingly none the worse. But the Swiss visitor must have thought twice before he again took a walk on that pleasant hillside. Happily he had no bones broken, but he was covered with bruises, and his clothes were torn to tatters.

One kind of Ibex is found in the rocky, mountainous parts of Arabia and Palestine, and especially in that tract of dry, stony country, which the Israelites had to cross in their prolonged journeyings between Egypt and the Promised Land. Such a home must suit these animals well, though no doubt they sometimes find the heat very trying.

Man is their enemy even in those desert regions. The wandering Bedouin with his long old-fashioned gun often takes aim at them. Sometimes he knocks over a young one, and takes it alive. You may buy it from him for about two shillings ; but it is not an easy pet to keep ; the chances are that it will pine away and die.

In a wild state the mother keeps the kids hidden away in some cleft in the rocks till they are strong enough to follow her. The Bedouin is only too glad to get one for his cooking pot, and even the flesh of a full-grown Ibex is reckoned very delicious food.

In that ancient book, the Book of Genesis, you may remember

A HERD OF IBEX ON THE MOVE.

[*Drawn by* COLBRON PEARSE.

how Isaac, when he
was grown old and
blind, begged his son
Esau to go out and
get for him the veni-
son he had always
been so fond of, but
which he could no
longer get for him-
self.

"Now, therefore,
take, I pray thee,
thy weapons — thy
quiver and thy bow
—and go out to the
field (*i.e.* the open
country), and take
me some venison ;
and make me sav-
oury meat such as I
love, and bring it to
me that I may eat ;
that my soul may
bless thee, before I
die."

No doubt you
know the whole
story — of the de-
ceitful trick that
was played by his
brother while he was
gone, and how the

THE ARABIAN IBEX.   [*Drawn by* JOSEPH WOLF.

THE ROCK-GOAT OF SCRIPTURE.

blessing was stolen, and how the huntsman-brother vowed
vengeance for the wrong that Jacob had done him.

But perhaps you do not know that the venison which Esau
went out to get, that day, was most likely the flesh of the Ibex.
For though we English, when we talk of venison, mean deer's
flesh, the only deer common in Esau's hunting country is the

gazelle, which as food is poor, dry stuff, and cannot compare for one moment with savoury Ibex meat.

In other parts of the Bible the phrase " wild goats " would more properly read " Ibexes." Our illustration shows what a noble-looking beast this Arabian Ibex is.

Indian sportsmen who want to win the splendid curved horns of the Ibex have to take very great trouble indeed. For that sharp-witted animal plays the game of " catch-as-catch-can " very cleverly indeed. He doesn't mind the cold, and he rather likes the rugged, ice-coated rocks ; and he can easily stand the glare from the blindingly white snow slopes. He takes care, therefore, that when man has a fancy for Ibex shooting he shall face all three of those uncomfortable things. " If you want me, you must come and fetch me," he seems to say.

And so the Englishman, who sometimes wants him very much indeed, says good-bye for several weeks to his pleasant bungalow in the south, and the kind of life he has been used to, and takes the train northward to the Punjaub. Thence he is whisked away in a jolting *donga* (car) to the far-famed valley of Kashmir, with its roses and blossoming apricot trees, its rich green fields and leafy forests.

All these he has to leave behind him and push on up, up into the mountain passes where the snow lies hard and deep, and far below him foaming torrents go rushing down to become broad Indian rivers.

And the Ibex is still a long way off even then. So the sportsman pushes forward, with his baggage and food on the shoulders of twenty or thirty coolies (native servants), till there comes a day when he reaches the bleak and bare valley shut in by snowy heights, which is the home of the Ibex.[1]

Yet the real difficulties only begin now. Few animals are harder to get near to than the Ibex of the Himalayas. All his senses are unusually sharp, and they are always awake. He is quick to detect the presence of an intruder by means of his eyes, his ears, and his sensitive nose. And when once he knows man is coming he is off like the wind.

[1] This word-picture of Ibex hunting is based on the actual experience of Mr. Joseph Clark Grew.

STALKING IBEX, IN THE HIMALAYAS.

ZEBRAS.

In the dim light before sunrise these animals straggle down to the green lower slopes, but as soon as the sun is up they climb back to the snow. There they stay till the hot light is again off the green slopes, when they venture downwards, and browse on the grass till nightfall. When scared, however, they can go for quite a long time without either food or water.

Then the Englishman and his brown-faced *shikari* (native assistant hunter) rise early one morning, and while the mountain-tops are beginning to catch the rosy light of dawn they steal out up the valley.

Now walking briskly, now with bent backs and heads down, one moment clambering between great rocks, the next crouching down out of sight, it is indeed no easy task to hunt the Ibex in his native wilds. The sentinels of the herd will give the alarm the moment they see anything moving.

But if the wind is blowing towards the hunter, and he can get, without being seen, under the shelter of some rocky ridge which the herd is making for, then indeed a golden chance may come.

All unsuspecting the herd comes stepping over the white tract of snow, the long beards of the males blown sideways by the wind, and their magnificent horns bending grandly over their backs. The right moment comes—the moment of danger for the best of the herd, the moment of reward for the hunter.

The latter has waited long. He has lain quiet in his stony hiding-place, half-frozen by the icy wind, and shivering with expectation. Will the herd turn aside ? Will his shot go wide ?

On come the dark, goat-like forms across the snow. A little nearer, and then two shots in quick succession, and the prize is won. The herd has scattered in wild alarm, but leaving behind them the two biggest of their number.

The shikari and his sahib (master) are soon stooping over their prizes. The horns of the one measure forty inches from tip to base ; those of the other, forty-four !

It is good to know that the game laws of Kashmir make it punishable for any one sportsman to shoot more than a certain number (six) of these splendid creatures.

But, after all, their best defence lies in their own alertness and the wildness of their home.

THE ZEBRA.

"ONE of the finest sights in all the animal world."
That is how the writer of a recent book on wild life in East Africa speaks of the great herds of Zebras which he saw on the wide plains. There they were, roaming over the *veldt* (grassy expanses), hundreds of them, grazing or galloping, or turning with heads thrown up and pricked ears to find out what was approaching them.

Like the wild ass of Western Asia, the Zebra of Africa is in a very special sense a freedom-loving animal. He knows well that man's coming usually means mischief, and directly any person appears in sight he flings up his hoofs and away he goes. He seems to say, like the American patriot, " Give me liberty, or give me death." He is wiry and strong, nimble and fleet.

If you have seen a Zebra at close quarters, you will know what a striking-looking creature he is, with his striped body and banded legs. And, strangely enough, he is fond of roaming in company with another curious-looking animal—the gnu, which is likewise

"Tameless, and swift, and proud."

Zebras love the plains ; they are not forest animals. The vast open spaces of East Africa, with their coarse long grass, rough scrub, and here and there a big shady tree or group of trees—these are just what suit them. If the plain runs up to the foot of a range of stony hills they like it all the better. If pursued, they will take refuge there. Off they go with a toss of the head, and a clatter of hoofs, racing up the slopes with a speed that soon leaves rider and horse panting far behind.

The Zebra has many enemies besides " the man with the gun," and has need, therefore, of all his watchfulness and his nimble feet.

One might think that with so many fierce beasts prowling about, especially at night, such a noticeable figure, as the Zebra seems to us, would be always in danger. Wherever he went, wherever he rested, he would be marked down by hungry eyes.

Now the strange thing is that it is only when he is taken away from his proper surroundings, and put on view, as, for example, at the Zoological Gardens, that he becomes conspicuous. At home, in Africa, it is often quite difficult to catch sight of him when he is standing still under some tree : the flickering shadows of the branches mimic so closely the stripes on his body.

ZEBRAS AT THE ZOOLOGICAL GARDENS.

Even when he is out in the open his black and white body blends wonderfully with the tall grass.

But it is at night, when his sharp-toothed foes take their walks abroad, that it is most important for him to escape notice. And surely the brilliant light of a tropical moon would " show him up " in a most merciless way ?

Yet, no ; hunters tell us that even when Zebras are only forty or fifty yards away, it is often impossible to see them, even in the broad moonlight. Nay, these animals have sometimes been so close to the hunter that he could hear them breathing, yet could not make out where they stood.

It sounds contradictory, but the truth is that the very stripes that seem to make the Zebra such a striking and noticeable creature, are really his best protection.

This was once proved, in a very simple but ingenious way, by Professor Ewart. He tethered a pony out in the open, one bright moonlight night, and he and his friends went fifty yards away. From that distance it was easily seen. Then he went to it and fixed black and white ribbons round its body, imitating as closely as he could the stripes of a Zebra. He walked back to his friends, and they looked again. The animal had vanished.

It is mostly at night that one hears the curious barking noise which Zebras make.

There are three distinct kinds of Zebras : Burchell's Zebra, which is the most common, a fine animal, with hoofs like iron ; Grevy's Zebra, which is rather larger, with very beautiful and complete striping, and which was only discovered about 1882 ; and the True or Mountain Zebra, which was the first kind known to Europeans, and which, though finely striped, is the least tall of the family. The small herds now carefully preserved in Cape Colony, where once it abounded, will soon be the only survivors of the True Zebra. There was another striped animal, similar to the Zebras, called the Quagga, which was also numerous once upon a time in Cape Colony. But the last of the herds was shot down about thirty years ago.

The Zebra of which we hear stories, from time to time, of its having been driven in harness is Burchell's Zebra. Its temper is not to be depended on, but it has allowed itself to be harnessed with mules, and also with ponies ; it has helped to draw waggons across the veldt in South Africa, and teams of four have been driven *for show* in England.

But the fact is, the Zebra is an animal not made for work. He is too restive, too wilful, too independent. Force him, when in harness, to go on trotting and pulling, and he breaks down. Most likely it was just so with the wild horse long, long ago ; but for so many ages he has been man's helper and fellow-worker that now he can keep on working hour after hour, and do the same day after day.

Nevertheless, in our British East Africa Protectorate, Zebra farms have been started, and some capital animals have been

A HERD OF ZEBRAS SCARED INTO A GALLOP.

[*Drawn by* COLBRON PEARSE.

bred and reared. Some of them will even bear to be saddled, and others are trained for other work. They have their own separate stalls in clean, airy stables, and a veterinary officer to doctor them and inspect them—just as if they were horses.

Zebras may be made to do various things, but nothing seems to tame their tempers. Ask any circus manager what he thinks of the Zebra, and he will tell you that he is one of the most difficult and intractable creatures you can have to deal with.

His jaws are like steel, and when he snaps at his keeper or his trainer, as he often does with little or no provocation, he can do dreadful injury. He kicks, too, most viciously. Tying up one leg is no remedy, for, standing on two, he will lash out with the other, and yet stand firm. Herr Schillings, the daring German hunter, thus writes : " I do not hesitate to say that it is less dangerous for a tamer to handle lions, tigers, and other such beasts of prey, than the Zebra with its fearful bite."

At the Zoological Gardens many anecdotes are told of this creature's spitefulness. Mr. A. T. Elwes, the veteran animal artist, some of whose drawings appear in this volume, has one such story, in his recent book on the Zoo.

Speaking of a pair of Zebras, he says : " Not long ago the male Zebra was seen dragging his mate round and round the enclosure by one of her ears, which he held firmly between his teeth. When at last he released her she nestled up to him with every outward show of affection, and then suddenly bit him sharply and kicked him savagely at the same moment, after which she raced away at the very top of her speed ! "

It would be hard to beat that for treachery and spite. And he goes on to mention an instance of another Zebra which without being provoked in any way, pushed through a sliding door, and rushed fiercely at a keeper. It knocked the man down and " pinned him by the leg until his cries brought another keeper to the rescue."

Altogether it seems as if the Zebra was one of those animals that are quite out of place in a small paddock. They need to be seen on the wide plains of sunny Africa, roaming in herds through the long grass, with the curly-horned gnus, whose temper is as short as their own.

THE LEOPARD.

CUNNING, fierce, and daring, the Leopard ranks next to the tiger among beasts of prey. He has not the tiger's tremendous strength, and he is nothing like so large; but he can do astonishing things in the way of killing and carrying-off, and in agility he is probably better than either lion or tiger.

Indeed, the quickness of a Leopard in darting and leaping, in twisting and turning, is wonderful. His spine is as flexible as that of an acrobat. His leap is like the flick of a whip, and if hunted he can spring out or disappear with a suddenness which is almost magical.

He has one accomplishment, too, which even the tiger cannot boast of—he can climb trees. We think of the tiger as a great striped cat, but the Leopard is far more cat-like. He will often pass the day in the cool shade of a tree-top, reaching his airy perch without any difficulty. His cry, too, is very cat-like, half mew, half snarl.

He is a truly beautiful beast, and as graceful as he is beautiful. It may even be doubted whether a Leopard skin is not as handsome as a tiger's, though it has not the rich colouring of "Stripes." The "black spots" are really very dark rosette-shaped marks, on a yellowish ground. These are not always the same in different members of his tribe. And, indeed, the yellow ground becomes so dark in many (quite black in some), that such are looked upon as a separate species, and named Black Leopards.

The Leopard is found both in Africa and in Asia, and he has cousins (the jaguar, the ocelot, and others), in Central and South America. Wherever he is met with he is apt to be a terror. He is crafty as well as strong, and he can worm that slim body of his through gaps in thorn-hedges and palisades which seem too narrow to need safeguarding.

His movements, too, are so quick that even in broad daylight

32

LEOPARD HESITATING WHETHER TO ATTACK.

3

a trained hunter with a modern rifle will find it no easy matter to hit him when he bounds away at top speed. And to hit without killing is a dangerous game for even " an old hand " to play.

For although a Leopard, as a rule, does not willingly fly at a man who has not molested him, it is a very different matter when he has been wounded or cornered. Then he is like a wild cat indeed. Weapon or no weapon, he turns and flies straight at his foe. His leap is of lightning swiftness, and if he can he will fix his sharp teeth in his enemy's throat. His claws rend and tear, and the wounds are terrible.

A recent African traveller, whose cool daring has been beyond all praise, says frankly: " A wounded Leopard is a most dangerous opponent . . . I can only advise the greatest caution in hunting these animals."

When he is caught —as very many Leopards are—in a trap, it is often risky to go near him unarmed. For if he is caught, say, by one foot, he will often spring up, wrenching loose the whole trap, and, despite the heavy weight, fly savagely at the intruder.

Sometimes the trap is baited with a live goat tied to the spot, sometimes with the dead body of some other animal liked by this spotted

A LEOPARD CUB FED ON BOTTLE MILK.
A NATIVE COOK IN MOMBASA FEEDING HIS PET.
[From a Photograph.

thief. Such food is not hard to find. He is partial to venison, and this can be had by obtaining an antelope or gazelle. He is a notorious poultry stealer, too, but a single fowl might not tempt him, especially if he has had the run of a hen-roost, and killed his twenty or thirty birds in a few minutes.

There is another kind of diet which pleases him—monkey's flesh : and he can get it for himself at any time if there are monkeys in the neighbourhood. He crawls up into the branches of the trees where a group of them are chattering and grimacing, and falls like a thunderbolt into their midst. Then, as he is seen making off with one of their number in his jaws, the chattering and screaming become ear-piercing, and very often the robber is hotly pursued.

Baboons, those strange dog-faced apes that are so numerous in South and East Africa, have a formidable enemy in the Leopard. They will often combine and stone him out of their neighbourhood. He is much too fond of dashing in among them, and picking up some fat little baby baboon which has ventured out of reach of its very watchful elders.

There are times when the Leopard does not come off scot-free. The great teeth of an angry full-grown male baboon, if once they are fastened in his enemy's body, are strong enough to injure if not to disable him. Or, as he springs at some tender fawn, the parent antelope—perhaps a gemsbok—may cleverly receive the marauder on the points of his terrible horns. Or one of the huge, thick-skinned, marsh-loving beasts—some rhinoceros, to wit—may resent his presence and, heedless of teeth or talons, trample him under its huge feet.

Man, too, has to be reckoned with. Not merely the European sportsman and naturalist, but also the native hunter with his traps and his spears. Indeed, nowadays, firearms can be got at a low price by these blacks, and then all animals, including Leopards, have a very bad time of it.

The Kaffir warrior used to look upon a Leopard-skin robe, with a fringe of Leopard tails hung round his waist, as one of his proudest adornments. And loud and long were the rejoicings over any one of these animals when killed and brought in.

A crowd would gather round and pour out on the dead body

BLACK LEOPARDS.

[*From a Drawing by* ERNEST SMYTHE.

THE CHEETAH, OR HUNTING LEOPARD.

[*Drawn by* GEORGE RANKIN.

plained that one of them had been bitten by the brute, and that it was always springing out on the goats and chasing them about. So the playful Snow Leopard was shipped oversea, and found a new home at Regent's Park, London, where many of its cousins had already been housed.

Long centuries before London possessed a Zoo, Leopards had been brought to this country.

Harrison, an old writer, tells us, in his *Descriptions of England*, that Henry I. "cherished of set purpose sundrie kinds of wild beasts, as bears, libards, ounces, lions, at Woodstocke and one or two other places in England, which he walled about with hard stone, in the year 1120, and where he would often fight with some one of them hand to hand."

There is one kind of Leopard which has long been trained to be useful to man. This is the Cheetah or Hunting Leopard. Its second name tells for what purpose it is trained.

It is found in Africa, but India is its chief home. There, it is quite a common sight at many up-country railway stations to see a Cheetah being carried to or from the train, chained to a sort of bamboo framework supported on the shoulders of four natives.

It is a tall, slim animal, more lightly built than the common Leopard. It has the usual spots, but the fur is of a reddish-fawn colour, and rather coarse.

There is a class of men in India who make a business of catching Cheetahs, and taming and training them. The modes of capturing them may differ with different districts, but one mode is simple enough.

It is well known that these animals are in the habit of paying visits to certain trees, for the purpose of sharpening their talons (a Cheetah's claws project much, even when sheathed and not in use ; hence they are constantly rubbing against the hard ground and getting blunted).

The natives take note of this, and having marked the particular trees resorted to, they quietly put nooses of raw hide round each tree. When, next day, they go to look at their snares they usually find one or more Cheetahs caught. The work of training is then begun.

The Cheetah is a born hunter, so that the trainer merely

has to teach him to obey orders and do everything at the word of command.

Six months is usually enough to bring the creature quite under control. He is not shut up, but chained outside like a yard dog, and he grows to be quite as gentle and teachable as an ordinary collie.

Well-trained Cheetahs will fetch a good price, and purchasers are not hard to find. Rich Indian princes are fond of them, and take pride in their cleverness.

Hunting with Cheetahs is a most exciting sport, though to us it seems cruel.

Several Cheetahs are driven on bullock carts to a place where deer are feeding in the open. The carts get as near as the watchful deer will allow. And then the sport begins.

The keeper unchains his spotted pet, and slips off the hood with which up till now it has been blindfolded. Quivering with eagerness, the Cheetah jumps down from the cart and begins to creep towards its distant prey. It slinks along behind stones and bushes till it feels near enough, when with a rush it flies out from cover, and with astonishing swiftness makes straight for the deer.

Then one of two things may happen. If the deer has not been on the alert, it probably knows nothing till the fierce beast has sprung upon it. But if the deer has taken fright early enough and bolted, the Cheetah may spring in too great a hurry—and miss. In that case, as if utterly ashamed of itself, it trots back to its keeper, who slips on its hood and chains it again to the cart.

Perhaps it was this kind of Leopard which was meant by an old writer who lived away back in the Middle Ages, and had the queerest notions about animals and their habits, which he had mostly got from hearsay. He says: " The Leopard is a beast most cruel . . . He pursueth his prey, startling and leaping and not running, and if he taketh not his prey in the third leap or in the fourth, then he stinteth [*i.e.* he stops], for indignation, and goeth backward as though he were overcome."

HUNTING ANTELOPES WITH THE CHEETAH.

THE GIRAFFE.

IN the long ago, before this earth of ours was trodden by man, all manner of gigantic and queer-shaped beasts lived and moved and had their being here. All have died out, leaving their bones in the river-mud and the earth-beds for puny man to examine and wonder at.

There is one creature, however, still with us that is so strange in shape and so oddly proportioned that it might well pass for a survivor from those ancient times.

This is the Giraffe. He is the tallest of all living beings, wild or tame; and of his eighteen or nineteen feet of height his neck and head represent about half. The outline of his body is one continuous slope downwards from his shoulders to his tail, so that his hind-legs seem much shorter than his fore-legs.

If a Giraffe is strange viewed at a standstill, he is stranger still as a runner. Indeed, the giant creature, when it moves off, is said to "give you the idea that it is likely to come to pieces." And someone else says: "Its tail is twisted over its back, its head and neck rock to and fro, as if they were on the point of separating from the body, and the hinder legs are thrown out sideways at every step, so that one sees the front legs between them." Could anything be more awkward?

When one thinks of its great size, and of its beautiful light-brown dappled skin, and its peaceful, timid nature, it is hard to understand how such a very conspicuous animal can possibly pass unnoticed by its enemies.

But the truth is, the markings on its skin are so wonderfully like the lights and shadows under a tree that often when a Giraffe is standing close in against the tree trunk, and keeps quite still, even the quick eyes of the African natives will not single him out. It is a case of what is called "protective resemblance," as we have seen in regard to the tiger and the leopard and the zebra.

But he is more likely to be found among the coarse, dry grass, out in the open, and here his long neck cannot be hidden. Yet his colouring seems to make him a part of his surroundings even there. Indeed, one traveller who took snapshots of many wild creatures in Africa, says: " Generally speaking, Giraffes are more difficult to photograph than any other animal." By which he means that they do not " stand out " from their surroundings.

It is, of course, very hard to get near them in any case. The author of a book about the Soudan and its tribes says: " They are very difficult to shoot, for their long necks give them a great advantage over a hunter, as they can see him long before he knows they are anywhere near. And thus they often make off without being seen at all. Also they have very keen scent."

A herd of Giraffes may be of almost any size. From fifteen to twenty is, perhaps, the most common number, but sometimes there will be but half a dozen, and sometimes as many as fifty.

The herd is always under the care and leadership of some old bull Giraffe, whose wariness it is hard to get round. His colour is nearly always rather dark, and Herr Schillings calls attention to the thickness of the neck, which is surprising to those of us who have only seen the lanky creature in captivity. It seems, in some of his photographs, to be swollen to twice the proper size.

Strange though it seems, it is a fact that the neck of a Giraffe, in spite of its prodigious length, is built of exactly the same number of tube-like bones as a man's neck—namely, seven.

Another peculiarity—a smaller one, but very noticeable—is the pair of queer little " horns " growing out of its head between the ears. Properly speaking, they are not horns at all, though it seems as if Nature had started making a pair, and had stopped short soon after they had " sprouted." They are covered with skin, and have each a little tuft of dark hair at the top. A third and much smaller knob is seen growing out of the forehead between the eyes, as if in imitation of the fabled unicorn.

As I have said, Giraffes are usually found on the sun-scorched plains among the long, dry grass, but one writer says that he has never seen them feeding on grass. Their natural food is the freshest and juiciest leaves of trees, not forgetting plenty of twigs; the acacia trees are great favourites.

When the dry season comes and the plains are parched with the heat, they do what Europeans dwelling in India do, or try to do,—they get away to the hills. The forests half-way up the mountain-side give just the refuge they want, and they have been met with as high as 7000 feet above sea-level.

Giraffes, more than any other four-footed creature, perhaps, deserve the name of dumb animals. Compared with, say, the dog, the horse is a silent creature; but the Giraffe seems really to have no cry at all. Even when struck down by the arrow or bullet of the hunter, it utters no scream of pain, not even a groan. But it is said that the pleading, reproachful look in a Giraffe's eyes as it lies wounded makes even a hard-hearted sportsman feel half sorry for his deed.

A good many Giraffes fall a prey to wild beasts; though even the lion may well think twice before springing on one of them, especially a bull. For

GIRAFFES DRINKING AT A POOL.
[*Drawn by* JOSEPH WOLF.]

4

the lightning kick of those sharp hind hoofs—sometimes ten and even twelve inches long—is enough to cripple or kill outright even the king of beasts.

It is man, however, who is to blame for the dreadful rate at which these strange and beautiful animals have been lessened in number.   In South Africa they are rarely to be seen now out in the open ; they have learned that to be safe they must keep to the wooded regions.   Indeed, we have it on good authority, that " these wonderful animal-giants exist only in large numbers in the vast East African plains, because they cannot be hunted there by mounted hunters on account of the climate."

The new kinds of rifle, which can send a bullet such an immense distance, and the new gunpowder, which leaves no puff of white smoke to show where the sportsman is firing from—these are deadly perils for all wild creatures that depend on their watchfulness rather than on their armour-like skin.

Certain native tribes, too, have much to answer for.   Some of them hunt the Giraffe for the sake of its flesh.   Others are tempted by the money offered for its skin by European traders. In one instance, no less than three hundred were slaughtered to supply a big order.

They are captured in many ways—shot down, killed with poisoned arrows, or taken by means of skilfully concealed pitfalls. These pits are dug out to a depth of some ten feet, with a ridge of earth running across them ; falling astride of this ridge or mound the Giraffe's long legs are helpless to enable him to spring out and get away.

The coveted skin of the Giraffe fetches as much as £5, so that the cunning native hunter finds it well worth while taking trouble to obtain it.   It is wonderfully thick, especially in the case of an old bull, where it often reaches one inch, and it is made into all manner of things.   Many an African warrior's shield is of Giraffe hide ; perhaps also the soles and thongs of his sandals.   Cut up into strips it supplies the long lash which the Boer wants for the whip with which he drives his waggon team of oxen.   The tail makes a capital fly-whisk.

Occasionally Giraffes are captured alive, and find a home in some foreign Zoo.   But it is a difficult creature to bring over land

A TALL BABY.

YOUNG GIRAFFE BEING FED BY ITS KEEPER.

[*From a Photograph.*

and sea. Many of them die even before they reach the coast. For the great long-legged prisoner finds it hard to trudge slowly over several hundred miles of sand and rock. And when he is shipped for Europe or America, sea-sickness, or want of the food he loves, may put an end to his life.

Our London Zoo for several years had no Giraffe. The regions where he is to be found were overrun by fierce fighters—the Dervishes ; and not until British and native troops under Lord Kitchener had met and scattered these Dervishes, and the country had rest and peace, could more Giraffes be got.

Once at the comfortable house and paddock provided for them, the long-necked strangers settle down, as a rule, and do well. Young ones, even, have been born there. So let us hope the Zoological Gardens will always have specimens of this gentle creature.

Those who go to see them there have sometimes had good reason to know what an extraordinary long reach the Giraffe has. A very common trick is for it to stretch its neck over the top bar of its enclosure, and neatly pick a flower from a gentleman's coat. Or—more disappointingly for itself—it will snap off an artificial flower from a lady's hat.

This is only doing what, in so much happier fashion, it does every day in its African home. For that long neck is not given to it for nothing : thereby it is enabled to dine on the very freshest and juiciest leaves, growing high up out of reach of animals less tall and erect.

And even more wonderful than the long neck is the long, flexible, snake-like tongue, which is almost as useful as a hand, in picking out and plucking just the leaves and buds which are best.

In captivity cut grass or dry hay, carrots, onions, and other vegetables are its usual diet, but in a wild state its favourite food is yielded by the camel-thorn and other sorts of acacia, the foliage of which it eats very daintily, carefully getting rid of every thorn.

As we have said, the Giraffes in Africa have been slaughtered by thousands during the last fifty years. Many of the places where once they abounded will see them no more. Native hunters and sportsmen from Europe have shot them down all too freely.

Happily something is being done now, though rather "late in the day." A Convention—attended by representatives of many nations—met in London in the year 1900, and the whole matter was talked over. It was felt that it would be a shameful and piteous thing if what is called the "big game" (that is, elephants, rhinoceroses, giraffes, zebras, and so on), and even many of the smaller wild animals, in Africa and elsewhere, were killed off. And so rules were laid down—with sharp penalties for breaking them— for protecting these wild creatures, and saving them from extinction.

NOTE.—Of the nations whose spokesmen signed that new order, Great Britain certainly has done her part; but some other nations have not enforced the law very carefully.

In December 1903 a number of sportsmen and governors met in London and formed a society with the same good object. And in June 1906 a deputation from this society had an interview with the Colonial Secretary. They urged the need of having the laws strictly carried out, and they made a number of very wise proposals which should go far to protect those animals which still roam wild in British Africa.

THE BUFFALO.

THE true Buffalo is not the shaggy-headed beast which once roamed the plains and prairies of North America in countless thousands, and was hunted down alike by Redskins and white settlers. That was the Bison. He, too, was a member of the great Ox-family, but he was really quite distinct both in habits and appearance.

The true Buffalo belongs to India and to Africa. Tamed and taught to be useful, the Indian kind is now found also in Egypt, Palestine, Sicily, Spain, Hungary, etc. He has travelled eastward as far as China and Japan and the Philippine Islands. He has even been taken over to Australia, where he was allowed at last to run wild, and was hunted for the sake of his tough hide. The African or Cape Buffalo is a pugnacious savage, and has never lent himself to man's service. But the Water Buffalo of India— there called the Arnee—though he, too, is a sullen creature, has become one of the most useful servants that man ever had.

THE INDIAN BUFFALO.

He is the picture of massive strength. "A huge, black beast, with no hair, a skin like gutta-percha, immense horns, sometimes measuring more than twelve feet along the curve, and set like a pair of scythes on each side of its head." He may measure anything up to six feet, at the shoulder.

His ordinary pace is slow and leisurely, but when he is roused he will put his head down and charge with speed and fury.

It is ages since the Hindoos took the wild Buffalo from his fellows, and made his very stubborn spirit bend to the wishes of his new masters. It must have been a bold thing to do. For even now centuries of training and control have left the "tame" Buffalo pretty much what his wild relations are. Outwardly he is obedient and peaceful, but let a stranger come near him and he snorts with suspicious dislike. And as for his natural enemy, the tiger, the sight or sound or smell of the great striped "cat" rouses all the savage fury in his Buffalo nature.

What the reindeer is to the Laplander, what the camel is to the Arab, the Water Buffalo is to the native of India.

For great tracts of India, as of China, are swampy ground, thanks to the big rivers, which bring down so much mud and slime ; and in these swamps rice is grown. But rice, like other crops, has to be cultivated, and the wet ground has to be prepared for it. No horse could pull a plough in such places, but the slow, mighty buffalo easily does so.

His broad hoofs keep him from sinking in the mud, though the latter is often so deep and soft that it closes over his hocks. Indeed, for pulling and hauling he is the strongest animal in the service of man—except the elephant.

He may often be seen plodding along the banks of a river towing some boat or barge, just like a canal-boatman's horse in England. And he is a capital swimmer, and will readily plunge into a river and swim across to wherever his work lies, on the further side.

In the Highlands of Scotland, the old people used to tell stories round the fire on winter nights about a dreadful beast—half animal, half goblin—called the Kelpie or Water-Bull. They told how it would start up out of the reeds and rushes by the side of some lonely loch (lake), as a solitary wayfarer went by, and nearly frighten him out of his wits with its deep bellow and tossing horns.

But if the Kelpie has died out in Scotland, he is "very much alive" in India. For in truth the Buffalo is a Water-Bull, and is apt to be a most frightening goblin if you come upon him unawares.

Sir Hugh Clifford, K.C.M.G., describes in a very amusing way what a scare he himself got, while out shooting snipe in the muddy rice-fields.

He was startled by hearing a loud splashing, and suddenly saw "a huge, ungainly monster, covered with mud from the water-hole in which he had been lying," leap out within a few yards of him. "The creature came forth scrambling and heaving, with all its four sturdy limbs straining under its weight." Getting on to firm ground, the Buffalo, for such it was, snorted with anger at the intruder with the gun, and glared defiantly at him. Then, very slowly and deliberately, it tilted up its head till its big horns

HEAD OF ARNEE.   [*From a Photograph.*

lay flat on its back, and looked at him " down its nose " with the utmost contempt and disgust.

Then, as he began to move away, the big, ill-tempered brute came after him. The panting sportsman was just wondering how many more mud holes he would have to flounder in and out of when a rescuer came in sight.

And who was the rescuer? A fellow-sportsman or a stalwart native with a sharp ox-goad? Neither. It was a tiny brown-skinned boy, with no clothes and no weapon. He stared first at the man running, and then at the snorting Buffalo, and at once understood.

He ran up to the great animal, and giving a little jump "smacked the creature in the eye with his tiny palm. Next he called it a strong name, hooked his fingers through its nostrils, and led the huge brute away, unresisting and ashamed of itself."

The little Indian boy, another writer has well said, is the Buffalo's tyrant and master. He leads the herd out to pasture, and brings it home again. Very often he rides all the way on the back of the leader of the herd.

In China the same thing may be seen. Mr. Oliver Ready, in his book *Life and Sport in China*, tells us it is quite a common sight to meet "one of these unwieldy, dangerous-looking brutes being quietly led along, by means of a thin string attached to his nose, by a wee native girl.

"When tired of walking, she stops the animal, draws down its head by the string, puts her tiny foot on the massive horn, and is slowly raised from the ground by the Buffalo, and placed gently on its back, which is so broad that she can kneel and play about on it while her charge is grazing."

These Buffaloes are well cared for, and most of them die after years of service, often through sheer old age. Mr. Ready once met a Chinese family returning from the funeral of their Buffalo! The creature was an old and valued servant who had been "in the family" for twenty years.

If Buffaloes are given work to do they will patiently do it, but you must not rob them of what, in human workers, answers to the "dinner hour."

A workman may spend this in any way he pleases. The Buffalo prefers to spend it standing in water, up to his eyes. And as his little master likes this way too, you may often see the pond or river dotted with the black snouts of the lazy creatures; and, on the neck of one of them, the upper part of a little brown figure with a cool turban wound round its head. If there is no work to be done, there they will stay till nightfall.

No one worries about the safety of these tiny herdsmen. If

A COMMON ROADSIDE SCENE IN INDIA.

they fall into the water there is no danger, for they can swim like a fish. And if a wild beast came out of the jungle, the Buffaloes would be more than willing to meet and kill the intruder. They will rush even upon a leopard or a tiger, and wreak their fury upon him—unless he turns tail before their fierce charge.

Indeed, so fearless are these strong brutes that sometimes when a tiger is known to be lurking in a strip of jungle, and will not come out, a herd of Buffaloes is driven through it. Up and down they march, shoulder to shoulder like soldiers in rank, till they come upon the tiger's hiding-place. Then they snort and charge, and the sportsmen coming up shoot the tiger dead.

A WONDERFUL ESCAPE. [See p. 65.

Tame Water Buffaloes differ very little from their wild fellows—either in appearance or habits. The wild Buffalo is one of the most dangerous animals in the world to hunt. If he is not killed or crippled by the first shot, he will make for the man who wounded him, and do his very best to gore and trample him to death.

THE AFRICAN BUFFALO.

He is no man's servant. Unlike his Indian relation, he is not one to be tamed and trained and harnessed.

In outward appearance, the chief difference between the two

lies in the shape of the horns. In the African or Cape Buffalo they have a most threatening look. They are much more curly, and the roots form a solid, bony mass covering the top of his head. From under this heavy mass peer out his little wicked eyes.

There is seldom anything but rage or suspicion in those eyes, except perhaps when he is enjoying his favourite mud-bath beside some pool or river. Even then, let him only catch sight of anyone passing by, and his anger flares up at once. One moment he is wallowing in lazy, pig-like contentment, up to his chin in the muddy water. The next, the startled traveller sees a great dripping beast with terrible horns and flashing eyes leap up out of the slime, and hurl itself upon him.

If the monster takes him unawares, he will dash his victim to the ground, then toss him on his horns, and gore and trample him till even his friends would not know his body.

You might almost fancy that, like those unhappy people of whom we read in the New Testament, this creature must be " possessed with an evil spirit." Most animals, it is true, are " snappish at times, but this one seems *always* in a bad temper, always resentful, always ready to do an injury. He sees in every passer-by an enemy, and makes it his duty to get rid of him.

His rage is a mad rage. He lowers his head and charges in the direction of whatever it is that offends him. The great craggy mass of horn over his eyes has often saved him from dashing out his brains, but it also hinders him from seeing well, and now and again a buffalo will blind himself by trying to rush through one of the terrible spiky thorn bushes which abound in Africa.

Sometimes Buffaloes in their wild rushes injure their own comrades. It is said that, in one instance, the big bull that led the herd stumbled and fell. Did the herd slacken their pace, and wait for him? Not they. They swept over him, killing him with their heavy tread, and leaving his body trampled and lifeless far behind them.

There is a story told of a native who had the same frightening experience. It is related by Lieutenant Victor Giraud in his book, *A Journey to the Lakes of Equatorial Africa.*

He and his party had startled into flight a big herd of Buffaloes. One man named Kauma, the native cook, had the ill-luck to be

CAPE BUFFALOES CHARGING A LION.

right in their way. He flung himself down on the ground, or was knocked down, and to the horror of his master the whole herd to the number of a hundred and fifty galloped over him. When they had passed, Lieutenant Giraud rushed forward expecting to find his servant a bruised and battered corpse.

" To my utter astonishment he got up of his own accord, shook himself, and felt himself all over from head to foot, and finally exclaimed—

"' Bah ! They *only struck my head* ! ' "

That great hunter, William Cotton Oswell, once found himself in the midst of an immense herd of Buffalo, excitedly dashing hither and thither. Many men would have been in terror for their lives, but what Oswell was most anxious about was whether he could get a steady shot at one of them. He confesses that all the time he was wondering why the enraged beasts did not knock him down and trample him flat as a pancake.

On another day he had a most narrow escape. He and his attendants had stumbled into the midst of a herd of Buffalo. Up they all got in a panic and went tearing off through the long grass where they had been resting.

But one old bull who had been fast asleep woke up very angry. He was not a bit inclined to run. On the contrary, he was eager to punish the disturber of his afternoon nap. Oswell nearly ran into him, but stopped in time and fired his one shot. It only wounded the enraged beast, who forthwith charged down on him. Quick as thought Oswell sprang up and caught a tree bough above his head, pulling his knees up to his chin like a good gymnast, and the great bull passed underneath him.

It is not so much his strength and fury that help to keep the African Buffalo from being exterminated. There are plenty of hunters bold enough to face and shoot him. But even if the numbers now to be seen in the better-known parts of Africa were all killed off, there are places where it is likely many would be found for long years to come. The truth of the matter is, these retreats are about as unhealthy as you could imagine. Marsh fever (malaria) lies in wait for the white man, and often— even if his health keeps up—he is stung by mosquitoes almost unbearably. " Millions of tiny ticks, also, which infest the grass

5

and brushwood, get on to his clothing and swarm over his body till the skin is all sore and inflamed."

Besides, the place itself is neither dry ground nor water, but a mixture of both. When the hunter pushes his way into the swamp he often finds that he cannot get forward, even by wading, because between the patches of reed-bed are deep muddy pools.

Many of these pools are haunted by crocodiles of all sizes, some of them being huge. They will seize a man when they can get him, and they lie in wait even for the Buffaloes as they stoop to drink in the shallows. Snapping at the noses they easily pull the great beasts down the slippery banks into the water, and devour them at their leisure.

Before the year 1890 there were plenty of Buffaloes in East Africa, but that dreadful cattle plague, the rinderpest, spread from the tame cattle to the wild ones, and thinned the number of the Buffaloes to a terrible extent. It is good to know that recent reports show that—thanks to the trouble taken to preserve them—these animals are increasing again, at all events in British East Africa.

THE REINDEER.

THE very name of this animal seems to call up a picture of the Far North. We think of a great dreary expanse of snow and ice, lit up by the flashing light of the *Aurora Borealis*, and, gliding across the snow in a comfortable sled like a big shoe, a round-faced Laplander. He is clad in furs from head to heel, and his steed is a fast-trotting Reindeer.

This wonderfully useful creature belongs, indeed, to the Arctic Circle. Bring him south and he will sicken and die. The cold which would make us shiver keeps him in health.

It is well for man that this four-footed servant of his is so hardy. For to the poor Lapp he is horse and cow, goat and sheep, "all rolled into one." When a Lapp dreams of growing very rich he pictures himself as the owner of a thousand Reindeer. Most likely he will have to be content with quite a small herd, but even a score or so will keep him from want.

Reindeer milk to drink and to make into butter and cheese; Reindeer horn to convert into all sorts of tools and implements; Reindeer flesh for meat; Reindeer hides to make into clothing, curtains, rugs, and wraps of all sorts; Reindeer sinews to take the place of cotton and thread,—what a list of uses for one single animal to be put to!

What the buffalo robe used to be to the American Indian and the backwoodsman and emigrant, the skin of the Reindeer is to the Lapp and the Arctic traveller. If you examine a good Reindeer skin, you will find the hair so thick that the skin proper cannot be seen, part the hairs as you may. No wonder, then, it makes a splendid covering for those who have to travel— and worse still to sleep out—in the searching cold of "the white North."

The Reindeer varies a good deal in size and height; roughly, he is about the size of a stag, but he has not the proud toss of the head which makes "the monarch of the glen" such a noble-looking creature. Still, if "handsome is as handsome does," the Reindeer ranks with the best. Whole tribes of people in the bleak northern lands would be at their wits' end without him.

His colour is greyish brown in winter, except on the neck and other places where it is white. In summer the fur darkens a good deal. A noticeable thing about him is the thick tuft of long hair on the throat, just like a beard.

The antlers are big, broad, and branching, and part of them are bent forward far over the forehead. Unlike most deer, the female Reindeer has horns as well as her mate.

His eyes are quick to notice anything, especially if he be a wild Reindeer, and suspects danger; his sense of smell, indeed, is sharper even than his sight or hearing.

Notice his feet. A deer's feet, as a rule, are sharp and narrow, but this hardy member of the deer clan has to travel more often over snow and ice than across grass or heather, or rough sandy tracts. That is why a Reindeer's hoofs are so "splay" and broad : it prevents them from sinking in the yielding snow.

These same hoofs are deadly weapons against the prowling wolf. A Reindeer is a good swimmer, too, and his broad feet are of great use in paddling him across a river, especially where the current happens to be strong.

The late Mr. Henry Seebohm, who spent much time and trouble in studying the wild birds of Siberia, has some interesting things to tell us about the Reindeer owned by the Samoyedes there.

They, like the Lapps, are a roving people, who live in encampments instead of building themselves towns, and, like the Lapps too, they reckon themselves rich or poor according to the number of Reindeer that each man owns. A good Reindeer is worth about a sovereign. Some Samoyede owners, we are told, have as many as ten thousand of these useful animals—an astonishing number, if it is true, and surely not easy to feed in winter.

When a Samoyede wants to pick out, say, twenty, thirty, or fifty Reindeer from his herd—perhaps to make a present of them, perhaps to sell them—he and his helpers use the lasso. They are very skilful in handling it, and nearly always manage to send it over the deer's antlers at the first fling.

Meantime, the dogs run barking at the herd, just like sheep-dogs, to keep them all in a bunch, and if one breaks out from the group and gallops off, the dogs go after it and head it back again.

On such an occasion, Mr. Seebohm says the scene is most exciting—the Reindeer racing round and round in circles, not

REINDEER HERDS IN LAPLAND.

A SUMMER ENCAMPMENT OF FRONTIER LAPPS.

willing to be caught, the white perky little foxy-faced dogs barking and yapping furiously, and the Samoyedes being driven to and fro in their Reindeer sledges, with lasso on wrist watching their chance to make a throw.

The lasso, by the bye, is a hundred feet in length, and is made (like everything else belonging to its owner, it would seem) from the Reindeer itself ; so, too, is the very harness in which the deer is driven. Instead of a whip, the driver uses a long pole, called a *toor*, with a bone button at the end : with this he pokes or hits his deer, should the pace not be what it ought.

But the Samoyede, like the Lapp, has little cause to complain of the slowness of his steed. Mr. Seebohm says of his own team : "Sometimes our Reindeer seemed to *fly* over the snow. During the last stage of our journey the pair that drew my sledge galloped the whole way without a pause."

Wild Reindeer are still to be found, but only in certain places. For they are too useful to be left running wild, where there is any chance of capturing them.

Liberty is sweet, but it is doubtful whether their tamed relatives do not lead a happier life than they, on the whole. A wild herd must always be on the watch, ready to stop feeding at a moment's notice, and go racing off.

Now it is a pack of snarling wolves : anon it is a Lapp hunter ; or, worse still, it may be an English sportsman, who has crept up unnoticed, and picks out the best deer in the herd, and lays him low before he can hear the *crack* of the deadly rifle.

But the sportsman who wants to "bag" a wild Reindeer must be willing to do some very rough climbing and weary trudging. For the deer's favourite haunts are among the dreariest places in Europe. They lie away at the back of the bleak mountain range that runs like a spine down the long peninsula of Norway. They are right up in the northern part where Norway and Lapland join.

To find the Reindeer at home you must trudge across great snowfields and clamber over, or through, barriers of jagged rocks, and wade through ice-cold torrents. The snow may be so wet as to soak your boots till they are sodden, and the wind rushes at you, cruelly keen, as you rest a moment on the higher ground.

It is here that the wild Reindeer is to be found, and lucky is the hunter who is able to creep up to his quarry without being seen or heard or smelt by this very alert animal. Often the tired pursuer gains the top of the last ridge only just in time to see the deer stop feeding, snuff the air suspiciously, and then go bounding away among the rocks, while the hastily fired bullet buries itself harmlessly in the snow.

It is hard to realise that there was a time when the hunting of the Reindeer took place in the British Isles and in Central Europe. Yet we have proofs of it. Its bones have been dug up in England here and there, and one relic of great interest has been found—nothing less than a picture of one of these animals.

It was drawn by some unknown artist ages ago. No painting, this ; brushes and pencils there were none, in those far-off days. It is scratched in outline on a piece of bone with some sharp tool, probably a pointed flint. Unmistakable it is—a Reindeer with the horns laid back along its neck. It is one of the rarest pictures in the world.

In winter, Reindeer—the tame herds, at all events—prefer the lower ground where the pine and spruce forests give them some protection against the bitter winds. Then their food is a kind of crinkly white lichen, known to us as Iceland moss. Even when this is deeply covered with snow, the Reindeer will find it out, and reach it by means of his warm breath, and strong hoof, and routing, poking nose.

The return of the warm weather brings pleasanter food, in the shape of juicy, green buds on the fir trees. But alas ! it brings also a terrible plague of flies, which make the Reindeer's life a misery. They bore into his thick skin and lay their eggs there, until he is covered with sores. His only remedy is flight. He and his companions gather in great herds and move off to the hills, and there they stay till King Winter's return has killed the mosquitoes and other winged pests in the old forest haunts of his tribe.

The Lapps are a roving people, and it does not take them long to break up an encampment and move off with their herds to a fresh place. For their own houses are mere huts made of wooden poles and wickerwork stuffed up with dry fern and birch twigs, easy enough to build.

All that is wanted for the deer is to mark out a space—say, about forty or fifty yards across, if the herd consists of three hundred deer,—and rig up a strong rough fence of birch boughs. Into this enclosure the animals can be driven, and here they can best be seen by a visitor.

An acquaintance of mine thus describes what he saw at a Lapp encampment, when he entered the deer pen :—

"The beautiful animals of all ages, from the sturdy old buck with his towering antlers and proud bearing to the frolicsome fawn of a few months or weeks, were moving gracefully about within the narrow space. I was never tired of admiring them.

"Here and there a man was seen going about with a light rope, which he threw round the neck of the deer which was to be milked. He tied the other end to one of the many birch trees inside the pen, and then one of the women came and milked the deer. The yield of milk is nothing like so great as from cows, but it is a delicious drink, being as thick and rich as the best cream."

A good deal of money must be made by the sale of smoked Reindeer tongues, thousands of which are sent to Russia, Sweden, Great Britain, and other countries, as an article of food.

As for the uses to which the living Reindeer can be put, they are very many, as we have seen. But first and foremost may be mentioned its wonderful power of drawing heavy loads for hours together, over slippery, uneven ground. The owner is forbidden by law, to pile up too big a burden, but, if required, a good Reindeer will trot for several hours, at nine or ten miles an hour, pulling behind it a loaded sled weighing close on 300 lbs. !

In a certain palace in Sweden there is, or was, a portrait of a Reindeer which made an extraordinary journey. It was in 1699. An officer had to carry important despatches between places 800 miles apart. He set out in a Reindeer sled, and made the journey in forty-eight hours. Those who wrote down the story added that the gallant beast fell dead on reaching the end of its "record run."

In the year 1892 Reindeer came to the help of a poverty-stricken people away in the north-west corner of North America. You will find it named Alaska in your maps. It is a wild and dreary region, and the winter cold is intense. Food was hard to get and still harder to fetch from the nearest Government station. Death and sickness were busy among these poor natives.

At last someone said, "Why not introduce Reindeer? They do wonders for the Lapps. They may yet save these poor Alaska tribes."

REINDEER.

The plan was tried. Sixteen Reindeer were brought all the way from Lapland and Norway. They throve well, increased in numbers, and now there are thousands there. Their native owners find them a perfect treasure. Missionaries use them in getting from place to place in their visitings. The miners (there is much gold to be got in Alaska) have their supplies brought up from the coast on Reindeer sledges. And the tough, fleet, untiring creatures are even used for carrying the mail.

That letters should come by Reindeer post will not seem strange to any American children who may read this. For do they not believe that Santa Claus comes in a wonderful sled drawn by a team of Reindeer that gallop through the frosty air over the white roofs of the sleeping town?

But this reminds us that North America has a Reindeer of its own. This is

THE CARIBOU.

It is a larger creature than its European cousin, but nothing like so tractable and useful. Indeed, even when caught it will not allow itself to be trained and taught. A wild animal it is, by nature, and a wild animal it prefers to remain.

It is a pity this is so. For the Caribou would make a strong, fleet, and enduring steed, if harnessed to a sled. The hunters and trappers who range the bleak and bitter lands lying round the great lakes of Canada know well how long a Caribou can keep going. Often they have to follow the creature for several days through the silent forest and over the snowy ground. Sometimes they come up with him, and he falls to their guns; but very often he makes for the frozen expanse of the nearest lake.

If once he gets a start on the ice there is no overtaking him. But the way he behaves is most odd: it must be almost as funny as a clown running a race at a circus. The Caribou sets off at a great pace, but suddenly something in front startles him; he pulls himself up, but the ice is too slippery. Down he goes on his haunches, and is carried in a sitting posture for some distance. Presently he scrambles to his feet, and rushes off in another direction, only to fall again and slide forward, and jump up. It is very funny to watch, but the weary hunter does not feel like laughing as he sees the fleet deer disappearing round a bend of the lake.

The dried flesh of the Caribou, when mixed with marrow, makes some of the best pemmican (dried and compressed meat made into cakes), and the skin provides a splendid outdoor sleeping-rug, keeping out both the wet and the cold.

A herd of Caribou may comprise anything from a dozen to two or three hundred, but the rifle-bullet of the white hunter and the deadly pitfall dug by Redskin and Eskimo have sadly reduced the numbers.

The Indians, indeed, have a great many clever tricks for decoying the Caribou. For, like most deer, they are very curious, and will often draw near to anything that catches their eye and sets them puzzling.

When caught and killed, the Caribou is put to many uses. Its flesh is valued food. Its hide can be tanned into leather for moccasins (leggings), or cut into strips to make thongs and straps ; with the fur left on, it serves for coat or coverlet.

The antlers can be split up into " heads " for fish-spears and fish-hooks ; and in one way or another every part of the dead Caribou " comes in handy " to the native hunter who is lucky enough to have captured it.

THE RHINOCEROS.

AN armour-plated animal! Really one might fancy that Nature had tried how near she could get to the making of such a creature. And what wonderful armour it is! Easy to wear, and not so stiff but that its owner can twist and turn about quickly, yet so hard that very often a modern rifle-bullet hitting it anywhere but in the right places, simply chips off pieces as it might from the face of a rock.

A frequent mistake of artists in drawing the Rhinoceros is to always give him the loose armour - like hide, whatever country the animal belongs to. As a matter of fact, it is only the Indian species that shows these massive folds of the skin.

There are several distinct species of Rhinoceros, and one has only to look at them carefully to see how they differ. It may be in the length of the horn or horns, or in the shape of the nose, or in the look of the hide. But they all agree in being tough-skinned and of very uncertain temper.

We all know the phrase " a good-natured giant." It is often true of human beings, and of some animals, as, for example, the elephant; but it is certainly not true as regards the Rhinoceros.

The keepers at the Zoo could tell you many a story of the blind fury which seizes their burly pets from time to time. One day they may be as lazy and tractable as could be wished; the next, they will turn savagely on their guardians, who have to make a quick bolt for one of the iron screens which have been provided in the corner of the stable as a refuge. And, in its wild state, the furious rushes which it makes upon the hunter who has disturbed it are the subject of many an exciting story.

The Zoo has usually had one or more specimens of this surly, hard-skinned, hard-natured beast.

As far back as the year 1513 a Rhinoceros was brought to Europe. It was sent as a present from India to Emmanuel, King of Portugal, who, as a devout Catholic, intended to present it to the Pope. But the great creature, after the manner of its kind, got into a rage one day, and managed, in some way or other, to sink the small vessel which had been chartered to carry it to its destination.

In 1685, during the reign of our King James II., another Rhinoceros was safely landed in England. And a little over a century later one was brought to this country from the East Indies, and exhibited in London at Exeter Change, where there was a small menagerie.

London was highly interested in the new arrival. We have the record of its habits and the amount of food it consumed. We are told that it ate 28 lbs. of clover, and the same amount of ships' biscuit, besides quite a heap of green vegetables ; and that it was given five pails of water two or three times a day.

Its thirst was equal to its appetite : it would quaff from its trough three pailsful without stopping. And it was not a tee-totaller either, for it was able and willing to consume three or four bottles of wine in a few hours. Its death was not due to gluttony, however, but to " getting up in a hurry," for it dislocated a joint in one of its front legs, and inflammation set in. It died after a nine months' illness, during which its calf-like bleating was quite piteous to hear.

A Rhinoceros seems almost too tough a beast to feel pain. But there is plenty of feeling under that armour-like hide. When, for instance, a Rhinoceros is shedding its horn—as a crab casts its shell or a deer sheds its antlers—the place where the new horn is about to grow is very tender and highly sensitive. So that when, in his touchy, impatient way, he butts at things that annoy him, forgetting how careful he should be, you may see him start back, as if he had had an unpleasant shock. It must be an immense relief when that ugly but useful " spike " has formed and hardened once more.

The Indian Rhinoceros sheds his horn about every five or six years. In his case the horn is massive, but often quite low.

His small cousin, in Sumatra, has two horns, one long, one short. In Africa there are several species of this animal, one of them, the Keitloa, also has two horns, but his most noticeable feature is the overhanging upper lip.

Herr Schillings says: " The shape of Rhinoceros horns varies greatly. Sometimes they are flat like swords . . . even in regions where round-shaped horns are the rule. Now and again the horns of very old cow rhinoceroses grow to the length of nearly five feet. Sixty-two and a half inches was the length of one

INDIAN RHINOCEROS AT THE ZOOLOGICAL GARDENS.

owned by Colonel Gordon-Cumming: it had belonged to a White Rhinoceros." Fancy the terrible weapon such a horn would be!

The White Rhinoceros (the colour is really a rather dark (grey was once fairly common in South Africa, but is now almost extinct. He is a big, massive fellow, next in size, indeed, to the elephant. Numbers were to be met with between the Zambesi and the Orange River, but nowadays the few remaining pairs would have to be sought for either in Zululand or the north of Mashonaland.

The Black Rhinoceros, so called, seems to reach its largest size in the districts south of the Zambesi. But there are plenty to the north of that river, and quite a number were met with while the Uganda Railway line was being pushed forward some years ago. " They did no injury to the coolies," Mr. Selous tells us, "except by frightening them ; indeed, they appeared rather to be stupid animals, perhaps because no other creature attacked them. For even the lion never meddles with a grown-up Rhinoceros."

In olden days strange notions were held about the " virtues " of Rhinoceros horn. In countries where kings lived in fear of being murdered by poison, goblets and flagons carved out of this kind of horn were in great demand. For there was a belief that such wine-cups instantly betrayed signs of poison either by "sweating" or by causing the wine to bubble up and run over.

Modern experiments seem to show that this old belief was little more than fanciful. But you may still see the Rhinoceros engraved like a crest or a trade mark, on the brass plate outside the Apothecaries' Hall, London.

Another use to which the horn of the Rhinoceros—the long-horned white species—was once put was the making of ramrods. Down to the days of the Crimean War and the Indian Mutiny the powder and bullet in a soldier's gun had to be rammed home with a straight, stiff stick pushed down the barrel or tube. And the long horn of the White Rhinoceros, sometimes four feet in length, supplied just the kind of material out of which such sticks could best be made.

A natural use, to which the horn is put by its wearer when living, was noted by a famous hunter of last century. He observed that when the mother Rhino had to guide her young one, in their walks abroad, she made her baby go on in front, and directed its movements by pressing her horn against the little one's side.

It is only of late years that the Rhinoceros has been hunted down in any large numbers for the sake of its horn. The slaughter of elephants had been so reckless that the supply had begun to run short, and this suggested to the trader that it might be worth

INDIAN RHINOCEROS AT THE ZOOLOGICAL GARDENS.

while to go after this other pachyderm (thick skin) who roamed in his thousands over certain parts of the African continent. And so the Rhinoceros was marked out as a beast worth taking some trouble to kill ; and the killing began.

The Rhino is far more apt to provoke the great enemy, man, than his water-loving brother pachyderm, the hippopotamus, who is really a very harmless giant, save when he is attacked.

For the Rhino hates the sight of human beings, and does not hesitate to show his hatred. Should a caravan pass his retreat he thinks it necessary to rush out and charge it.

On one occasion a Rhinoceros came rushing down upon one of those big covered waggons which are so much used in South Africa. It had got stuck in the deep sand, and apparently the natives who accompanied it had seized the chance of doing a little cooking. They had built a fire and hung the iron pot over it, and were reckoning on sharing in a savoury meal.

The huge and massive brute charged the waggon with a crash, his horn splitting a hole in the boards. The shock was so great that it lifted the heavy waggon out of the rut, from which the oxen had been trying to haul it, and drove it forward several paces.

Then catching sight of the fire he rushed at it, knocked over the boiling pot, and tossed the burning faggots right and left, and finally went on his way, the iron-tipped spear of one of the natives rebounding lightly from his sides.

Steedman tells a story of another Rhinoceros charge.

A Hottentot who had won fame as a bold elephant-hunter, was one day riding along when a Rhino rushed upon him out of the thicket. Lowering its head the monster got its horn under the horse and tossed steed and rider clean over its back. The horse must have been fatally injured, but the Hottentot survived to lament having had no chance of shooting his assailant ; for the brute rushed off without troubling itself to make a second attack.

William Cotton Oswell, the friend of Livingstone, had a similar experience. He was stalking two Rhinos, and seeing one of them move towards him he waited to get a good shot.

6

But he waited a little too long. He fired, but the shot had little or no effect, and the great beast tossed him. He lay insensible for some time, and when he recovered found long red gaping wounds on his thigh and body, some of them five inches long.

On another occasion Oswell was attacked by a White Rhinoceros which he had mortally wounded. It got up and drove its horn through the horse to the saddle, and tossed horse and rider with its remaining strength.

A recent writer with a wide experience of Africa names as the five most dangerous wild beasts to be met with there—the lion, the leopard, the buffalo, the elephant, and the Rhinoceros. He hesitates to say which involves the most risks, but the difficulty of hitting the last-named in any soft place seems to point out that animal as being the most formidable.

Few things, he says, are more scaring as you are going along, than suddenly to see the great unshapely mass, with its threatening horn and little wicked eye, rear itself out of the mud of some pool or swamp where it has been lying, and, after staring at you for half a minute, come thundering down upon you, offering no chance for a bullet, even if your gun is loaded and ready.

As to jumping aside as he plunges past, that is easier said than done ; and this writer doubts a good many of the stories in which the sportsman's nimbleness at the last moment has saved him. He thinks the Rhino's nimbleness would be the greater, and that the terrible horn would be very unlikely to miss its victim. " The agility and quickness with which the huge beast moved, I shall never forget," he says, in speaking of the way a bull Rhino got up when shot.

Its sense of smell is almost as keen as its movements are quick, and the hunter has to take the very greatest care to get to windward of the animal. Should the wind veer and blow towards the Rhino, good-bye to all chances of stealing up undetected. The head is flung up, the sensitive nostril snuffs the " tainted " air, and then one of two things may happen. The Rhino may turn tail and bolt, or he may come charging down to find out where the enemy lurks, and kill him.

But it is not only by his keen scent that the Rhinoceros is guarded. There is a certain small bird, called the Rhinoceros-bird, which feeds on the thousands of ticks which pester the giant, boring into the soft parts of his great rough coat and setting up painful sores.

When a Rhino is resting, these friendly birds may be seen by the dozen perched on his body, hard at work. But they have quick eyes, like most birds, and the instant they see suspicious movements in the distance they break out into noisy twittering,

AFRICAN RHINOCEROS AT HOME.

and begin fluttering their wings in an excited way. At once the huge fellow rises or half-rises to his feet, and judges for himself whether it is a false alarm or genuine danger.

A herd of Rhinos is seldom met with, though as many as eight have been seen together. It is perilous enough to have even two to deal with, if they show fight.

Herr Schillings, who went to Africa not merely to shoot big beasts like the Rhinoceros, but to photograph them and learn their habits, had many adventures with these huge creatures. Perhaps the most exciting of all was this the following:

He had been trying all one morning to get a good photograph of a herd of giraffes, but they were too shy for him to get near enough to them. Suddenly he espied, about a thousand yards distant, two Rhinos out on the veldt. They settled down under a tree, and creeping up to within 120 yards of them he squatted down behind a low anthill, and took several successful photographs of them.

But the keen scent of the two animals soon made them aware of the presence of man. They got up, faced about towards him, and he had just time to snapshot them in this attitude when they threw up their heads angrily and came charging down to where they knew he must be.

He thrust the camera into the hands of one of his native servants, seized his rifle, and fired six shots in succession. They fell twice, ploughing up the sandy soil, but each time regained their feet, and came on.

His rifle empty, the intrepid hunter sprang aside to put a brier bush between him and the two monsters. They had the wit to charge one on each side of the bush, thus making sure of their victim, and he felt certain that his fate was sealed.

But like the strong Highlander, in Sir Walter Scott's poem, who, just when he had his foe at his mercy, sank down fainting from his wounds, so the two Rhinos collapsed almost at the moment they were about to kill the man who had wounded them. For him it was indeed a most narrow escape.

According to this sportsman there are still "hundreds of thousands of Rhinoceroses" on the mid-African veldt, but he thinks they are bound to "go" as civilisation, like a great incoming tide, rolls nearer and nearer to their wide feeding-grounds.

They are fond of retiring, however, to the impenetrable thickets on the slopes of the hills, and the hunter—whether he be European or native—knows well that to follow them into these thorny retreats is one of the riskiest things he can do. For the monsters often remain quite motionless until you are close upon them, and then rise from their afternoon sleep or their mud-bath with a suddenness which sets your heart beating and your hand shaking. And often the light also is none too good for taking aim.

For those of us who wish that Africa may long keep its great beasts, it is good to know that there are such places where the " man with the gun " cannot easily come.

Once, long, long ago, the Rhinoceros browsed and wallowed and fought in European countries ; he was a great hairy-coated fellow, and has left his bones not only in our English soil, but as far north as Siberia. But his descendants have no love for our grey northern skies and cold winds, and they are found only in Southern Asia and in Africa. Besides, there is no room in Europe now for the great surly, armour-plated monster, who hates the sight of man.

THE ELEPHANT.

HE is the lordliest of all created beings, save man. He is a giant in girth and stature ; he is a giant in strength. His skull is so thick that it will resist any ordinary gun-shot, but the brain inside it can reason almost like a human being. His little eyes will twinkle with fun, but where can you match him for dignity ? And as for his anger it is terrible. He can tramp up a mountain road with a cannon strapped on his broad back, but he is a nurse you may rely upon if little children are left to his care.

Where is there his like, in all the animal creation, for strength and intelligence, for humour and kindliness, together ? Set him beside his two fellow-pachyderms (thick skins) the surly rhinoceros and the clumsy, lazy hippopotamus, and how he " shines " by contrast !

We do not wonder that from earliest times man had his eye upon him, and that having hunted him for many generations it occurred to him to capture the burly giant, and try to tame him and turn his strength and cleverness to good account.

The princes of India have kept trained Elephants for two thousand years and more, using them as part of their royal state, and also as aids to their armies.

Long, long ago that warlike Assyrian queen, Semiramis, is said to have dreaded them greatly when she was going to invade India. She tried to be even with her opponent by rigging up a host of make-believe Elephants which were nothing more than black ox-hides stuffed with straw and carried on camels. All went well until the dummy Elephants and the real Elephants came together in the shock of battle. Then great was the panic and confusion, and the warrior-queen fled wounded and worsted, barely escaping with her life.

Ivory is often spoken of in the Bible, yet there is no mention whatever of the animal whose tusks and teeth supplied the ivory. But in the span of history which lies between the end of the Old Testament and the beginning of the New the animal is prominently mentioned.

Those were the days when there arose a family of heroes, the Maccabees, who led the Jews in a revolt against their foreign rulers, the Syrians. The latter had great armies of horsemen and footmen, and, above all, they had a number of Indian

INDIAN ELEPHANTS AND THEIR NATIVE DRIVERS.

Elephants. Fifteen hundred soldiers, says the old historian, were appointed to go with each Elephant; "wherever the beast was, and whithersoever he went, they went also; and upon the Elephants were strong towers of wood, filled with armed men, besides the Indian that bestrode them."

The Jews hated and feared these new and formidable foes. So Eleazar, one of the Maccabees, resolved to teach his countrymen that even those huge creatures were not invincible in spite of their towering size and their thick hide. He crept under one of them and drove his weapon into the soft part of its body. It was a gallant but rash act, for he sacrificed his life ; but the deed had the desired effect.

Another famous mention of Elephants in ancient history is in the story of Hannibal the Carthaginian, who was one of the greatest leaders and generals the world has ever seen.

He set himself to invade Italy, and actually brought his army over the snowy passes of the Alps. He lost nearly half his men, but with the remnant he came safely down into the green valleys on the sunny southern side, and won victory after victory. There were no proper roads over the mountains then, and all the world has wondered ever since at that great feat.

For not only were there horse soldiers in that army, but actually many Elephants. I think there must have been a fellow-feeling between the worn-out shivering soldiers, as they huddled together at night for warmth, and the poor shivering giants that had been brought from Africa to frighten a Roman foe.

Many years afterwards, the Romans grew quite familiar with the sight of Elephants. The animals were brought over and trained to perform the most surprising tricks, in the arena. Walking on ropes, dancing, mimicking a dinner-party, tossing and catching balls or spears, were among the tricks with which they delighted the huge audience gathered in the amphitheatre.

Haroun Alraschid, the Caliph of Bagdad whom you all know through the *Arabian Nights*, once sent an Elephant as a gift to Charlemagne, who is also the hero of many a romantic story.

Later, our own King Henry III. received a similar present from the King of France. Great was the excitement caused by such a visitor ; he was deemed to be the first Elephant ever seen in England. The Sheriff of Kent was ordered to go to Dover to arrange for his passage across the Straits.

Then further orders were sent to the Sheriffs of London, commanding them to prepare a suitable house for the royal animal, at the Tower of London ; it was to be forty feet in length, and twenty feet in breadth ; and they were " to find for the said Elephant and his keeper such necessaries as should be reasonable and needful."

Equal care has to be taken of the Elephants that come to our shores nowa-days, but we find better quarters for them than His Majes-ty's Tower.

Exeter Change, the old menagerie building in the Strand, London, was a favourite place for them to be

A FAVOURITE AT THE ZOO.

on show at the beginning of last century, but ere long the Zoological Society prepared room in their now famous Gardens, and their first Elephant was installed in the queer old thatched house and enclosure which did duty until 1878. Then the present spacious and airy house was built, and the Zoo Elephants became—especially to the children—one of the chief attractions of the Gardens.

Some of these Elephants have become quite important personages. Their names have been household words, and when, becoming unmanageable, they have had to be sent away, more fuss has been made about the matter than would be made over the death of a Prime Minister or a Commander-in-Chief.

Everybody has heard of the ridiculous outcry that took place when the famous " Jumbo " had to be parted with. Grown-up people behaved in the most foolish way about it. They scolded, they pleaded, they argued ; they filled whole columns of the news-papers with indignant letters ; they tried to get the law to interfere.

When it was known that, spite of all, Jumbo was really going away, loving gifts of every sort were showered upon him, from boxes of sweetmeats to bottles of pickles. Indeed, it seemed as if the people had gone mad more thoroughly than the Elephant.

Even when it had been decided to send him away, it was no easy matter to persuade such a monster to leave his old quarters. At last a strong wooden box on low wheels had to be made to take him. Thus caged, a team of stout dray horses hauled him, one March evening in 1882, down to the Docks, where he was taken on board ship and carried across the Atlantic to gladden the eyes of American boys and girls at Barnum's "Greatest Show on Earth."

While we are talking of Elephants on exhibition, I may mention the very funny case of one which belonged to a travelling wild beast show. The story is told in Mr. Elwes' book on the Zoo. Elephants are well known to be fond of rolling themselves in the mud when they are in a wild state, and as captives they will use " the next best thing " to roll in if they cannot get mud.

This particular Elephant found a big tub of treacle. It felt soft, cool, and slimy. "The very thing!" he thought, and forthwith he smeared the sticky fluid over his body. He then retired to his stable and had a good roll in the straw. Imagine what the effect was! A hedgehog ten feet high, would have borne some likeness to him.

The worst of it was that he was due to go into the ring to perform! If the manager had let him enter the ring the audience would have wondered what on earth the creature could be. And he could not be cleaned down because it was winter and the good wash which he stood in need of would have given him cold.

So there was nothing to be done but to cut him out of the programme, and, says the narrator, " he had to be left for nearly three months in a stable in a small country town, where he spent most of his time with his head out of the window, trumpeting loudly ! "

The stories told of Elephants belonging to " wild beast shows " and travelling menageries are numberless, and many of them are very amusing.

An Elephant, belonging to a large circus, once visited the town of Hythe in Kent. He was quite young, and attracted many admiring looks. One tradesman, a greengrocer, came forward with an apronful of potatoes, and the little creature helped himself to them with much relish.

SCRUBBING THE BABY.

A MORNING TOILET AT THE ZOOLOGICAL GARDENS.

[*Drawn by* WALTON CORBOULD.

Eleven or twelve years passed, and the Elephant again found himself in Hythe. He remembered the place well; also he remembered the greengrocer's shop and the feast of potatoes. So between three and four o'clock in the morning he managed to let himself out of his stable and found his way to the right street and the right shop.

The shutters were up and the owner upstairs asleep, but the visitor was not to be denied. He butted the door till it gave way, shouldered himself in, and had made a huge hole in the stock of fruit and vegetables before the keeper arrived, hot-foot, to scold him well and lead him back to headquarters.

But an Elephant's memory is proverbial. We all know the Eastern story of the tailor who pricked the inquisitive Elephant's trunk with a needle, and who was soused with dirty water, long after, when the mindful creature again passed by.

It is pleasant to know that the 'cuteness of the Elephant is not only shown in remembering old injuries, but also in quickly understanding when something painful or unpleasant is being done only for its good.

An English officer stationed at Calcutta was the owner of a very fine Elephant. Latterly it had suffered from a disease of the eyes, which grew worse, till the great creature could no longer see. Its master went to a certain Dr. Webb, who, after careful examination, told him that he thought the disease could be cured, but the remedy would be a painful one, and he doubted if the Elephant would stand it.

To his surprise and delight the blind giant felt so much relief after the first day's treatment, that when the doctor came again it lay down of its own accord, curled up its trunk, and drew in its breath just like a human being about to endure pain. When the stuff (nitrate of silver) had been dropped into each eye, and the worst of the smarting was over, the great patient beast scrambled to its feet, and tried its best to make the doctor understand how grateful it was.

The one distinguishing thing about the Elephant, compared with other animals, is its long flexible proboscis or trunk. Someone has called it a snake-hand, and, indeed, the Hindu name for Elephant is "*Hát'hi*," which signifies the "creature with a hand."

Without his trunk, an Elephant would be more helpless than a man with both his hands cut off. He can do all manner of things by means of it, and the soft sensitive finger-like end of it is of the greatest use.

In a wild state, for instance, he is most particular in picking and choosing his food, whether it be fresh green leaves or perfectly ripe food. And it is by means of the delicate " feeler " at the end of his trunk that he selects leaf or fruit, snapping it off with a twitch, or, if necessary, putting a coil of his trunk round it and breaking the stem forcibly. He can pick up a nail or a pin with it, and should this delicate member be hurt in any way he suffers terribly.

The long trunk itself is a wonder. It is, remember, no mere quaint appendage, but a most necessary part of his body, without which he would be likely to starve. If he tried to reach even the ground plants with his mouth, he would have to go down on his knees, for his short thick neck would ill serve him. And even then his tusks would be sadly in the way. As for the dainty leaves and fruits above his head, he would not be able to reach them at all.

But by means of that long, lithe, curling, twisting trunk he can fetch down the high-growing fruit or leaves without raising his forefeet from the ground, and carry the juicy foods to his mouth with ease and quickness.

It is the same with his drinking. A couple of tubes run all the way up the inside of the trunk, and he uses them like a suction-pump, drawing up the water of pool or river, and spirting it into his mouth. If he feels inclined for a shower-bath, he stands in the water and draws up trunkful after trunkful, squirting it backward over his broad body. This is quite a favourite amusement of his in the wild free life he leads in the Indian forests.

The flexibility of the trunk is astonishing. Thanks to the extraordinary number of muscles in its framework—some forty or fifty thousand—he can twist and turn it in every direction. Indeed, it entirely makes up to him for his clumsy, thick-set body.

That body is the very picture of solid strength. His forehead is like a rock. Indeed, the weight of the head, with its hanging trunk and long curved tusks, must be enormous. So Nature has propped the massive body on four pillar-like legs of great thickness.

The stiff straight look of these made the ancients believe that the Elephant had no joints in his legs. An old monkish book of the Middle Ages which I have on my shelves says: "For among other doings Elephants lie never down in sleeping; but when they be weary they lean to a tree and so rest somewhat."

Let us now see what distinguishes the Indian branch of the family from the African branch.

———

THE INDIAN ELEPHANT.

In the olden days when Rome was fighting her way up to the proud position of mistress of the world, her great rival, Carthage, sent against her more than one big army in which were many war Elephants.

Now, Carthage was a city of Northern Africa, and it is hardly likely that she would have borrowed these animals from Asia when in the wild country to the south there were so many to be had for the capturing. Yet to-day the Indian Elephant is the only kind that is the servant and helper of man, the African species being considered far too fierce and intractable.

But there are also outward differences between the two kinds. The Indian Elephant has much smaller ears than his African cousin. Also you may notice that his forehead is hollowed, while the African's is arched. And whereas he may measure ten feet at the shoulder, his relative is usually a foot taller.

It is chiefly in his trained cleverness that he puts his great ramping African relative into the shade. All the thousand and one stories that you have heard of "Elephant sagacity" have to do with the Elephant of India.

Probably the great beast was first used simply as an ornament— to march in processions on grand occasions. What more imposing sight, for example, could an Eastern monarch wish for than to pass to his palace by a roadway lined with these great patient stately brutes, decked with flashing ornaments, and caparisoned with rich trappings of various colours ?

In time these same royal Elephants would be taught to salute their master, perhaps by flinging up their trunks all together at a signal, or by going down on their knees at a touch from the Mahouts (native drivers) seated astride their short thick necks. Or some more elaborate movements would be gone through, as their trainers learned to trust them and depend upon them.

Then the enormous strength of the great creature would suggest its being used in the moving of heavy loads, and such-like work. And so while some Elephants would be reared and trained for royal state, others came to be trained as working-class Elephants, pulling and hauling, fetching and carrying all their days.

There are more Elephants, wild and tame, in the British Empire than in any other part of the world. They carry burdens that no horse or camel could even stagger under. Up to quite recent times they accompanied our warlike expeditions, some-times even across the sea, cannon and ammunition boxes being strapped on their broad backs. In the army we sent from India in 1868, to bring to book the cruel King of Abyssinia, there were no less than forty-four Elephants.

Perhaps those whose work is of a humbler kind enjoy life quite as much as the army Elephants.

Those, for instance, who are taught to "handle" the great balks of wood in the timber yards, seem to take pride in their service. The long sinewy trunk is their chief "tool," but when a heavy log has to be lifted and carried, they get it balanced on their tusks first, and then coil their trunk round it.

Mr. Rudyard Kipling's soldier, home from Burmah, recalls the days when he used to watch the great sensible creatures at work in the teak yards down by the river—

> "Elephints a-pilin' teak,
>   In the sludgy, squdgy creek,"

where the warm, damp air and heavy stillness is apt to take the strength and "go" out of the human labourer.

INDIAN ELEPHANT AT HOME.

A SCENE IN A CEYLON FOREST.

7

Here the four-footed giant works, at the bidding of his puny, brown-skinned, white-turbaned master, who sits on his back and directs all he does. Not only can he lift the logs, but he can arrange them as well, piling them in the proper way. On a level road he will carry half a ton, and make no complaint.

As a rule he is well treated. Indeed, he is too valuable a servant (and too costly a one—his food-bill is a big one) to be mishandled. And he *needs* to be carefully looked after, too. That thick wrinkled skin of his, which seems too tough for getting hurt, requires to be watched. Harness soon chafes it, especially in wet weather. He is liable to sore places—in his trunk and mouth, in the soles of his feet, and on the ridge of his back, and the sores soon get worked into ulcers, which mean that he has to be put on the sick-list for months together. Also he is apt to suffer from inflamed eyes. So, altogether, the giant does not make a wholly satisfactory workman.

The number of tame trained Elephants in India is, however, very large indeed. This working army is recruited from time to time from the herds of wild Elephants which still roam at liberty in the great forests of that vast country.

The catching of these is an exciting business, though not always so dangerous as you might imagine. Several ways of capture are used, but perhaps the most common is by driving them into an enclosure called a *keddah*, which is an open space fenced in with a high and strong stockade.

When the Prince of Wales visited India in 1905–6, the Maharajah of Mysore entertained him with a grand Elephant drive in the Kakankote forest.

For no less than two months before the day, 500 native beaters had been closing in upon the forest Elephants from a distance of fifty miles and more—surrounding them as with a ring that shrunk every day to a smaller size. Every Elephant they came across they scared and drove in towards the centre, until the whole herd was gathered on a little hill not far from the royal camp.

The Maharajah and his guests took up their position behind a leafy screen close to where the Elephants would pass. Perfect silence had to be kept. Then suddenly at a given signal the beaters set up an unearthly din on all sides of the hill, and the Elephants rushed past bellowing and snorting, to find themselves in the keddah, and the gate shut down behind them.

Here a number of tame Elephants with their mahouts were waiting to help in bringing their wild relations to submission and obedience. Sometimes they belaboured them with their trunks ; sometimes they hustled and squeezed them, one on each side of a captive. Others they simply held with their trunks while the nimble jungle-men slipped in and out among the giant feet, and cleverly passed loops of thick rope round the wild Elephants' legs, tying the other end to stout tree-stumps.

Some of the captives always take it very badly and resist to the last. Others with true Elephant intelligence seem to understand almost at once that resistance is hopeless, and resign themselves to their new state. These are rewarded and encouraged by the natives left to wait on them, with food of a kind they specially like ; and fourteen days is often quite enough to " break them in " to complete obedience. The ropes are then unhitched from stump or tree, and the quiet beast is led away to his new home, where he soon gets to trust and love the man who is told off to be his keeper.

Occasionally an Elephant thus captured and tamed will break away, and return to the forest and the old free life.

There is a story of one, owned by a grandee in Calcutta, in eighteenth-century days, who was much attached to her keeper, but found the call to freedom too sweet to resist. She escaped, and the keeper was accused of having sold her to make himself rich. Despite his denial, he was condemned and severely punished.

One day, twelve years later, he was sent out with an Elephant-catching party. A herd was sighted, and the hunters prepared for a capture.

Suddenly the man recognised one of the beasts as his old charge, and called to her by name. She came out from the herd, threw up her trunk as in a glad salute, and knelt down before her old friend. Not only was he able to bring her back in triumph, but she enticed her three calves to accompany her.

The man on his return told his strange story. It proved his innocence, and his old accusers did their best to atone to him for the wrong they had done him. As for the Elephant, she became the property of Governor-General Warren Hastings.

A word must be said about the far-famed White Elephants of Siam and Burmah which play such a part in court ceremonies (Lord of the White Elephant is one of the high-sounding titles conferred by the King of Siam).

Strictly speaking, they are not white at all, but a sort of dingy pink, and often even this is confined to the front and breast, the other parts being the ordinary brown-grey.

One of these was exhibited at the Zoo, soon after the notorious Jumbo had been sent away, and those visitors who expected that a White Elephant would necessarily be really white were grievously disappointed.

This Elephant came from Burmah, having belonged to the retinue of the drunken King Theebaw whom we had to dethrone in 1885.

In that green land of Burmah well-nigh every White Elephant found in the forests became royal property.

If to live " in a golden state " could make up for the loss of their old liberty, such Elephants ought to have been happy. For they were treated with as much reverence and consideration as the half-mad emperors of old Rome, Nero and Caligula, treated their favourite horses, which they shod with gold and lodged in houses of gold, and commanded the people to regard as sacred.

In like manner these White Elephants at the old court of Burmah were housed in most costly buildings, ate their food out of silver troughs, and walked abroad hung round with trinkets of gold and festoons of jewels.

So expensive was the upkeep of a White Elephant that when the King wanted to impoverish any of his subjects, he used to present him with one of these royal beasts. As the feeding of an ordinary Elephant, say, in Ceylon, keeps a couple of men busy cutting leaves, you may guess what the feeding and tending and housing and decorating of a royal White Elephant would mean to any man who was not more than ordinarily rich.

That is the origin of the saying you may sometimes hear : " A handsome gift ? Yes, but I think it will prove a veritable White Elephant." In other words, " It is a gift that will prove both useless and ruinous."

---◆---

THE AFRICAN ELEPHANT.

He is distinctly different from the children's favourite, the Indian Elephant. He never becomes man's servant, and to children he would be a terror. He is only wanted for the sake of his ivories—the great tusks and teeth for which he has been hunted from the earliest days.

Nevertheless, he is a grand beast, and true king of the African forest. To see him threading his way through its tangled depths, drawing that enormous body of his almost silently through the network of leaves and branches, is a marvel.

And to see him in a rage—to be in his path when snorting and screaming with trunk flung high, and his huge ears flapping wide like loosened shutters, as he bears down upon whatever has offended him—is to face a terrifying sight indeed.

In such moments he charges in almost blind fury, and before his onset the wiry bushes are trampled flat and stout young trees are snapped like kindling wood.

He must be a man of iron nerve who awaits that charge. Nowadays bullets are made which are big enough and hard enough to stop the rush of that mighty mass ; but sometimes the gun misses fire, at the second shot, and then there is nothing left for the unhappy hunter but to run. And that is usually a vain remedy, so swiftly do those thick legs cover the ground.

Such was the dreadful position in which Mr. Arthur Neumann found himself, on one occasion. In his book he tells how his gun failed him, and the Elephant, mad with rage, overtook him just as he threw himself into the brushwood to the right of the path and tried to wriggle out of sight.

Down she went on her knees, striding over her enemy and

HARD PRESSED.

ELEPHANT HUNT BY NATIVES ON AN AFRICAN RIVER.

fiercely pounding him with her massive head, and trying three times to gore him with her tusks. He remembers lying and wondering quietly *how* she meant to kill him, being quite sure that his last moment had come.

Presently she got up and went off to find her calf, leaving her victim lying bruised and wounded, but alive. His right arm was stabbed through, his ribs crushed in, and his face and chest also were badly hurt. But he recovered after many months, and lived to write the story of his adventures and escapes in East Equatorial Africa.

A somewhat similar thing happened to a hunter of an earlier day, William Cotton Oswell, but with a happier result. It was in the year 1850, and he had followed an Elephant which had retreated into the dense thicket along the banks of an African river.

Suddenly the giant doubled back on its pursuer, and the startled horse threw its rider and bolted. Oswell fell right in the Elephant's path, and lay face upward. He parted his legs, and, as he says, "saw the burly brute from chest to tail as he passed directly over me lengthways, one foot between my knees, and one fourteen inches beyond my head—and not a graze!"

It was a marvellous escape, and a most rare one. But, to lie still and helpless while five tons of flesh and bone stride over you is something to remember for a lifetime. And Oswell, intrepid hunter though he was, did remember it. "One hears of night-mares," he writes; "well, for a month or more, I daresay, I had *night-Elephants*."

The destruction of African Elephants during the last hundred years, nay, even during the last half-century, has been simply awful. It has been estimated that the ivory sent to England alone represents the killing of thirty thousand Elephants every year.

The European trader's coming to Africa marked the beginning of bad times for the great beast with the long branching tusks, and since that evil day the slaughter has increased. At one time there were tens of thousands of Elephants in West, East, and South Africa. Now there are only a few left in the whole of

Cape Colony, the chief herds having been preserved by law in the Zitzi Kamma and Knysna forest.

Even in Central Africa, where the Elephants seem to have finer tusks than in the south, the numbers have also been thinned. The habit they have of herding together and keeping very still by day, roaming only by night, makes it often very difficult to guess correctly how many are left.

Elephants are always on the move. The craggy, rough slopes of mountains and the slippery mud-banks of a river are no hindrance to these active giants. Moreover, they move from place to place with a swiftness that is simply incredible—especially if their suspicions are aroused and they think man is on their track. When the ground is dry the thud of their huge feet can be heard a long way off, but during the rainy season they seem to skim along almost noiselessly.

They detect the coming of a human intruder not by their eyes, which are comparatively weak, nor yet by their hearing, but by their wonderfully keen sense of smell : they throw their trunks high and turn the tip about in every direction till they catch the wind that blows from the point of danger. This trunk-waving is most odd to watch.

One who, of late years, has laid low many a tusker, says : " No sportsman who has hunted the Elephant much in Africa has got through without some serious mishap: many have been trampled upon and have paid for their boldness with their lives." And the same writer says : " The more one comes into contact with African Elephants, the more one is on one's guard ; for the hunter can never know what an Elephant may not be up to the next moment."

Away in the Soudan, a wandering tribe of Arabs, the Hamrans, has earned a reputation for daring and skilful hunting of big game. Whether all the change and bustle of Lord Kitchener's war against the Dervishes has scattered the tribe, I am not quite sure. But, be that as it may, you may read all about this race of hunters in Sir Samuel Baker's *The Nile Tributaries of Abyssinia*.

They hunt the Elephant, sometimes on foot, but more often on horseback, and the risks they run are great. They have a

THE WAY THE HAMRANS HUNT THE ELEPHANT.

special mode of attack of their own, and the huge creature goes down before it.

The hunting party of two, three, or four men follow the track of an Elephant in the early part of the morning, and time themselves to come up with him just when he is growing drowsy with the heat. If he has actually fallen asleep, the hunter slashes with his sword at the Elephant's trunk and sometimes severs it, so that the poor animal bleeds to death in an hour or so.

But, if he is still wakeful, the hunter creeps round at his back, and delivers his stroke at the hind-leg just above the heel. It is a most crippling stroke, and if the great creature does manage to stagger to his feet, he usually falls and gives the hunter a chance of dealing him another blow on the other leg.

" The swords used by the Hamrans," says a friend of mine who has been out in Africa, " are long and straight, and of a pattern supposed to be copied from those brought into the country by the Crusaders, long centuries ago. They are kept ground to a razor-edge."

Our illustration shows graphically the manner in which the Hamrans tease the Elephant and tempt him to follow one of their number, while the others seize the chance of getting in one or more strokes with the keen sword.

It is a risky way of hunting the African Elephant, and " accidents " are many. But you cannot attack a giant without danger, and this is a well-armed giant who, if only he could reach his nimble foes, could crush them as easily as we crush a moth.

THE HIPPOPOTAMUS.

BEHEMOTH he is called in the Bible, River Horse the old Greeks named him, as did the Romans after them, and in his native Africa he has yet another name—Kiboko.

He is the clumsiest of all animals that walk this earth, yet, when he cares to, he can run with a speed which makes an un-armed man doubt whether his own heels will carry him out of danger fast enough.

He is the most unshapely of beasts—a barrel-like body sup-ported on four very thick short props—and when he walks his feet are so far apart that he makes two tracks instead of one. Yet he is excellently adapted by Nature for the life he lives and the work he does. And though he looks hog-like in his slow, heavy, lazy movements, the hunter who comes upon him afloat in lake or river, often finds that the big fat fellow manages to see a very great deal without being seen himself. Kiboko has sharp wits, and brain enough to be exceedingly watchful and wary.

Long ages ago there were Hippopotamuses living and feeding and growing fat in the swamps and rivers of Europe—many even in this England of ours, as the bones (turned to fossils) dug up in the "brick-earth" found in some districts round London plainly prove. But since the days of history they have only come to Europe as foreign visitors, and much against their will.

Seventeen hundred years and more ago fine specimens of this huge ungainly creature were brought to Rome from North Africa (which, you may remember, was then part of the great Roman Empire), and exhibited in the Flavian Amphitheatre.

They were brought over by order of the Emperor Commodus, who was so vain of his prowess as an archer and javelin thrower, that he used to go down and fight in the arena like a common gladiator. He liked nothing better than to have a crowd of wild beasts let loose in that enclosure, and himself stand and shoot them down, while the thousands of spectators shouted their applause at his wonderful marksmanship.

But we hear of no other Hippos being imported until the middle of last century, when, thanks to the help given by Abbas Pasha, Viceroy of Egypt, a baby Hippo was captured by a party of hunters and conveyed on board ship to England. It was only three days old, and had been found among the river-reeds at Obaysch, on the White Nile.

HIPPOPOTAMUS AT THE ZOO (Afloat).

Young though it was it weighed fifty or sixty pounds, and it gave trouble to its captors from the very first.

The leader of the party, delighted at his good luck, caught up the " baby " and prepared to bolt with it before its parent returned. But it gave a squeak and a wriggle, and in an instant it had slipped from his arms and was trundling off into the reeds towards the river. The man had forgotten that the body of a Hippopotamus is protected against the water, in which it spends so much time, by a sort of natural oil, which makes its thick dark skin as slippery as an eel.

Frantic lest it should escape, the hunter rushed after the tough little beast, and harpooned it with his spear, which had a bent spike like a boat-hook.   Nothing else would have served the purpose.

But here began a long series of difficulties.   The baby Hippo proved a most inconvenient passenger to convey.   It took no less than four months to get him to Cairo, where he arrived under the protection of a lieutenant and a squad of ten black soldiers.   The cost of bringing him was generously paid by the Viceroy.

The troublesome infant was then sent on to the British Consul at Alexandria, and thence shipped to England.   He was named Obaysch after his birthplace, and under that name he was received as an honoured guest at the Zoological Gardens, London.

His keeper, Hamet, came with him.   Great was the attachment of the animal to his friend, and when Hamet slipped away from him by day or night Obaysch was restless — sometimes decidedly noisy and violent—until he came back.

Great was the interest and excitement aroused among the public by the arrival of this " distinguished stranger."   Crowds flocked to see him waddling to and fro in the May sunshine, with his huge jaws opening and closing, or floating idly in his tank with only his ears and protruding eyes above water.

That was in 1850.   In July 1854 another Hippo arrived to keep Obaysch company.   She was four months old and weighed over a ton.   She loved music, and when her keeper on board ship, an Arab snake-charmer, used to drone out his monotonous Eastern sing - song, she would listen with evident pleasure, swaying her big body to and fro.

Obaysch seems to have settled down easily, hardly remembering the freedom he had lost so early.   He lived for twenty-eight years after his arrival at the Gardens, and his mate lived four years longer. Their offspring, being born on a fifth of November, received the name of " Guy Fawkes," and is still living (or was until recently), though grown old and feeble.

An amusing story is told at the Zoo about this animal and its keeper.

It appears that the former, becoming restless and noisy one sultry night in summer, had been allowed out, and, rejoicing in the liberty and fresh air, had rushed down to its tank. The keeper happened to come along shortly after, and, as he looked at the cool still piece of water, he thought : " My charge is safe inside the stable, and there is no one about. The tank has just been cleaned out and refilled, and a plunge would be very refreshing."

No sooner did the idea come to him than he acted upon it. It was all very

HIPPOPOTAMUS AT THE ZOO (Ashore).

dark and still. The next minute he was out of his clothes. Over the strong railing he climbed, and into the water he jumped.

But instead of the cool splash he expected would follow, he found himself sprawling on the back of something broad and slimy that started violently, and sank to the bottom.

The poor keeper, nearly frightened out of his wits, paddled hastily to the side and scrambled out, panting and quaking with fear of the unknown monster in the pool, while the poor startled Hippo, whose quiet bathe he had thus so rudely disturbed, watched with great relief the pale-skinned sprite disappear over the railings.

The Hippopotamus is a peaceful beast even in his free state, on the rivers and lakesides of Africa—except when he is interfered with by man. His burly form and hog-like movements have gained for him a bad character. He has been called sullen and ill-tempered ; but Herr Schillings, the famous hunter and photographer of African beasts, has recently told us that " these animals are only ill-tempered and aggressive

8

when they have been pursued by men and several times wounded.''

This hunter mentions that often when he made his camp on patches of ground encircled by swamp, the Hippopotamuses would come round it with their great heads out of water, sniffing inquisitively. They might easily have come up and trampled through the hunter's tent, yet they contented themselves with inspecting it from a little distance. They were not shot at, and they did no harm. One big fellow even came up out of the water, one night, and walked right into the camp, and went back again without disturbing any of the tents between which he passed.

But, once roused, a Hippo can be a very formidable foe indeed.

The hide of a Hippopotamus is an inch and a half thick in places, but there are '' vital spots '' which the hunter knows of, and at these he fires with deadly effect.

Very often, however, when the creature is shot in the water, it is difficult to be sure that the bullet has taken effect. For the great beast usually dives if he is merely wounded, and sinks if he is killed. If he is only frightened and hurt he will come up to breathe some distance away, showing so little of himself that his black nose pushed above the surface might easily be mistaken for a drifting leaf or piece of bark.

If he is dead, the body will not rise for an hour or more ; then it floats, and is soon seized upon by crocodiles and birds of prey, unless speedily towed away by the sportsman, and dragged ashore by the willing hands of the natives.

They have their ways of killing Kiboko, but these are very different from the white man's way. If he is to be sought in the water they will paddle out in their canoes, or man a light raft and let it drift into the midst of the herd. Then the most deft spearman of the crew rises to his feet and drives his spear or harpoon, with all the strength of his arm, deep into the body of one of the unsuspecting giants.

Sometimes he misses his aim, and then woe to the luckless party ! The great head lifts itself up out of the water, and the enormous jaws open, with all their array of huge yellow teeth—a terrifying sight. The next instant they have closed on the canoe or the raft, and literally bitten it in two. Happy are the boatmen if they escape by swimming to shore, for those great teeth could even more easily cut *them* in half.

But usually the spear finds its mark, and, maddened with pain, Kiboko dives, dragging with him the cord which is secured to the harpoon. The other end is soon made fast, if possible, to some riverside tree or rock, and then, though he may snap

HIPPOPOTAMUSES IN AN AFRICAN RIVER.
[*Drawn by* J. WOLF.

the line, he is assailed by a shower of spears every time he comes up to breathe; till tired out with many wounds he can neither fight nor flee, and with much shouting and rejoicing the enormous body is dragged to shore or on to the nearest sandbank.

Mr. F. L. James tells us that when he was in the Soudan, and his companion had shot a bull Hippo, his Arabs were delighted to get the flesh to eat. He says: "After they had gorged themselves with as much of the fresh meat as they could manage to swallow, they cut the rest into strips, and hung it in the trees. When dried the meat was put into skins, and afterwards cooked and eaten from time to time. The fat, when boiled down, served us very well for cooking butter. . . . Altogether you cannot please your Arabs more than by shooting one of these useful animals."

Even more valuable is the tough skin of the Hippopotamus. Its chief use is to be cut up into long strips, softened and made flexible with oil or grease, and made into whips. The dreaded *kourbash*, with which the oppressed natives of Egypt used to be forced to work (in the bad old days before England undertook to govern the country), was made of Hippopotamus hide. So was the fearful *giraf*, with which the unhappy subjects of Theodore, the brutal King of Abyssinia, were often cut to pieces. So, too, is the stinging sjambok which the Boer farmer used so freely—a great deal too freely—on the " niggers " in his employ.

Altogether we may be sure that Kiboko after death has been the means of giving far more pain than he ever caused during his lifetime.

But if that is true, it is also true that he can be accused of doing an immense deal of " damage to property." We all know how much mischief a few cattle can do when they happen to get into a cornfield. But think of the havoc which a herd of twenty or thirty, or more, of these enormous animals can effect when at night they come up out of the water, and make a raid on the ricefields or other crops owned by the riverside tribes.

It is not easy to deal with intruders so formidable. But the natives set their wits to work and do their best to stop these " after dark " trespassings.

The favourite way is also the simplest. They dig a pit—a series of pits, indeed—in the track used by the Hippopotamuses (it is easy to find it, as you may suppose), plant a sharp stake at the bottom, and then cover the mouth of the pit lightly over with grass and boughs.

When night falls, the clumsy river-horse and his friends come blundering through the long grass, and one after another three or four of them tread on the pitfall roofs, which give way beneath their weight and let them through.

It is, of course, a cruel, painful death. But if we had to change places with those riverside natives, and had seen our little

A SHOT AT A HIPPO.

harvest half-eaten and half the rest trampled into mud by these great beasts, we should rejoice when, lying awake in our poor huts, we heard the dull crash that told us our trap had done its work. And we should waste no tears in pity next morning, when the huge body was hauled out, and we received our share of the delicious (?) fat underlying that tough hide.

Another mode of capture is to stretch a cord in the path along which the intruders will come. The cord is connected with another hung over the bough of a tree, and from which dangles a very sharp spear weighted with a heavy stone. The animal stumbles over the cord half-hidden in the grass, and brings down upon his head or neck the weighted spear-point.

Sometimes the trap is made still more deadly by smearing the weapon with a strong poison; so that even if the great creature tears himself free, the poison does its work ere long, and he falls dead not far from the trap.

It takes a good deal to make a hungry full-grown Hippo feel fully satisfied. His stomach can take five or six bushels of vegetable food, and the expense of " keeping " him at the Zoo runs up rather a serious bill.

But that is the fault of meddlesome man for putting him there. Nature never meant him to spend his life in a stable with a pond outside it. She placed him among the rank vegetation of African lakes and rivers, some of which get almost choked with the fast-growing water-weeds. Kiboko lives on these; so that when he tears up the great lily-like plants with his powerful lower teeth, he is not only collecting his own food, but clearing away what is apt to become a nuisance.

One does not think of the Hippopotamus as having anything to do with salt water. But it is known that those which inhabit the mouths of great rivers often float and swim out to quite a surprising distance from land.

It is very likely that they enjoy the change from fresh water to briny, as the salt must help to kill many of the parasites which infest their skins.

There are far fewer of these unwieldy animals now than there were even five-and-twenty years ago. No longer are they found in the land of Egypt where once they were so common. The sportsman there who wants to find one now has to go up the Nile beyond Khartoum. There are few, if any, south of the great Zambesi River. And their numbers have been thinned in almost all parts of the great African continent where once they were found from the mouth of the Nile to the Cape of Good Hope.

But the Big Game Protection laws will do something to hinder their destruction by sportsmen and natives alike ; and the widespreading swamps of West Africa, with their tangled thickets and lurking marsh-fever, will give them shelter long after they have become scarce in the better-known regions, east and north and south.

THE LYNX.

"LYNX-EYED"—we use the phrase when we mean that some-one is so quick-sighted that nothing escapes his notice.

The Lynx is quick-sighted, and it is much more. Its claws are as sharp as its eyes, and its frame is sinewy and well-knit. It is the largest member of the cat tribe now left in Europe ; its length from nose to root of tail is about three feet—the tail itself is but six or seven inches long. It runs rapidly in an odd series of leaps, its four feet striking the ground together ; and it can not only scramble swiftly up a tall tree, but race along the boughs after its prey in a way that only the most agile woodland creatures can defy.

The forests of Britain hold no Lynxes, but on the Continent they are far from rare, though scarcer in some countries than in others.

By reason of their habits they are not frequently seen, for they sleep by day and prowl by night, as a rule. The Lynx has a trick, moreover, of lying flat along the tree-bough or ledge of rock when it sees or hears a possible enemy drawing near ; and it often needs an eye as keen as its own to detect the crouching form, lying motionless, but noticing everything.

If attacked, or suddenly disturbed, by a man, a Lynx, like a wild-cat, may prove a very awkward customer to tackle. Its talons and its strong sharp teeth can inflict serious wounds. But if it interferes with man it is usually by way of his property—it " plays the wolf " among his flocks on the hillside. In South-Eastern Europe the shepherds have many charges to bring against the Lynx, and the same story of its mischievousness is to be heard in Norway and Sweden.

In places where the lambs or the kids of the flock are too well looked after to be safely stolen, it will prey upon hares and rabbits, squirrels, and occasional birds—indeed, these are its natural food.

THIBETAN LYNX.

COMMON LYNX.

The Lynx hunter is best pleased when he captures his quarry in the winter woods, for then it is wearing a much more beautiful coat of fur.

Some naturalists look upon the Lynx of Southern Europe as a separate species, but it seems likely enough to be the same animal as that which lurks in the more secluded Alpine forests and those of Russia and Scandinavia.

THE LYNX.

In a poem by Robert Browning, about an Arab physician in the time of Christ, and the strange things he had seen and heard in Palestine, an adventure with a Lynx on the road to Jericho is told in a couple of lines :

"A black Lynx snarled and pricked a tufted ear,

I cried, and threw my staff, and he was gone."

This was a Caracal, the name of which comes from a Turkish word meaning "black-eared." Except for its ears the fur of a Caracal is a pale brown, sometimes a reddish brown, but the under parts are much lighter, and there are certain patches of white about the under lip and chin.

This Lynx is found both in Africa and Asia, and though it has often been tamed, and even trained to hunt for its master, it has in general rather a bad character, and is reckoned ill-tempered and suspicious. It feeds on birds and small animals, and is said to pull down the fawns of antelope and deer. It is not much of a runner, but in quick bounds it comes up with its prey, and teeth and claws very soon do the rest.

Perhaps the most wonderful power it has is that of springing suddenly into the air when a bird is flying past : six and even seven feet is quite a common height for a Caracal to leap. And when, having stalked a group of birds strutting upon the ground, it jumps and lands in the midst of them, its strong, quick-darting paws deal out death right and left.

It has been known to kill nine or ten pigeons in this way, at one swoop. When we remember how quickly a flock of pigeons rises and scatters at our approach, we may guess with what lightning swiftness the paws of a Caracal do their deadly work.

The Siberian Lynx is so fond of solitude that the hunter usually has to seek for him in the depths of the great forests of that land. And even if the right place is reached the man may have to return without the coveted fur.

For the animal is not common—just one here and one there— and it is so quick-eyed and quick-eared, *and* so "knowing," that traps are of little use. The sportsman must trust to his dogs starting one, and to his own steady hand when it is time to bring the rifle to the shoulder. He may miss, and if the Lynx retaliates by springing at him, he may get very badly clawed indeed.

North America, too, has its Lynx. Like its Old World relatives, it loves the lonelier forest regions, and here and there it takes up its quarters on some unfrequented mountainside.

Some years ago, I read of an adventure which befell a young school teacher in the United States. He had been appointed to a village school in the northern part of Michigan, and when he arrived, late in the afternoon, at the little wayside station, he found that the village lay some miles away. He struck out in what he believed to be the right direction, but darkness overtook him and presently heavy rain began to fall.

Looking about for a place of shelter he espied a group of rather "tumble-down" shanties which had once been part of a lumber-camp. They were quite deserted, and he made for the nearest and pushed his way in at the door. The door slammed to, and latched itself.

The young fellow, already rather nervous, did not like the notion of being shut in. But as he was groping for the fastening, he was still further frightened by a queer sound, half snarl, half growl, which came from the far corner of the room, and which he heard above the wind and rain that were howling outside the cabin. He felt sure it must be some wild beast, though of what kind he could not guess.

Drawing off his jacket, all but the left sleeve, and wrapping it round his arm and shoulder, he gripped his clasp-knife in his left hand, and holding his revolver in his right he peered into the darkness and stepped forward.

Then, with a scream, the creature sprang at him. It fixed its teeth and claws in his well-protected shoulder, and tried hard to get at his throat. He fired every shot in his revolver into its body, and still it clung snarling and biting.

Dropping his empty revolver he struck with his short knife again and again, and then losing his balance he tripped and fell, striking his head with stunning force against the wall.

When he recovered his senses, daylight was peeping into the cabin. The animal—a Lynx—lay dead beside him.

Faint and burning with fever the young teacher managed to open the door, and slowly made his way back to the little wayside station, whence he was driven over to the village.

His adventure soon got known, and he found himself quite a hero, as the Lynx had been "wanted" for several years, but had baffled the cleverest hunters of the district.

THE LION.

" THE King of Beasts "—that has been the Lion's proud
title from earliest times. He was looked upon, in olden
days, as the embodiment of all that was noble and
majestic and courageous, of all that was mighty and terrible.
Other animals might make their attack by stealth; he came
openly, disdaining to creep and crawl.

In the old book of monkish lore which I have once or twice
referred to, I find this quaint saying about him : " In peril the
Lion is most gentle and noble, for when he is pursued with hounds
and with hunters, the Lion lurketh not nor hideth himself, but
sitteth in fields where he may be seen, and arrayeth himself to
defence. And runneth out of wood and covert with swift running
and course, as though he would account vile shame to lurk and
to hide himself."

From our earliest days we have all known the story of Samson,
the Old Testament hero, killing with his hands the Lion that came
roaring at him as he went along one day alone and unarmed. And
the old Greeks taught their children a similar story, of how *their*
Samson, the fabled Herakles, slew a ferocious Lion which preyed on
the people and the cattle of the green valley of Nemea.

In pictures and statues of this hero, you may see him leaning
on his great club, with the Lion-skin hung about his shoulders.
There are no Lions about Nemea now, and very quiet and peaceful
it looked when I saw it some years ago. But even down to the
days when Greeks and Persians fought at Salamis there were
plenty of these fierce beasts in the north of Greece. For we are
told that in Thrace they lay in wait for the Persian army camels
and killed many of them.

Lions were often " on show " in the amphitheatres of Rome
and other cities while the Cæsars ruled the world. They came
to take part in the horrid " games " of the arena, being set to

AN AFRICAN KING.

[*Drawn by* GEORGE RANKIN.

fight with one another, or with other wild beasts, or with gladiators armed with sword or spear. In the dreadful days of the persecution of the Christians, men and women, boys and girls, for the one crime of being found faithful to their Lord and Master, Jesus Christ, were sent to die by the jaws and talons of these fierce beasts, whose keepers had purposely kept them without food so that they might rush more ravenously on their victims.

Commodus, one of the Cæsars, to whom I have already made

A KING IN CAPTIVITY.

reference in a previous chapter, distinguished himself, it is said, at one of these exhibitions of wild beasts by killing a hundred Lions with a hundred arrows, one after the other. A wonderful feat for the royal bowman, if the story is true.

In mediæval times the Lion easily kept his reputation of being the kingliest of wild beasts. We all know why our own Richard I. was called "*Cœur de Lion.*" At Creçy and Poictiers and Agincourt—fields of glorious victory—the royal banner of England bore three Lions embroidered upon it. And at Bannockburn the standard of Robert the Bruce showed the great red Lion rampant of Scotland as its sign. Books of heraldry, the science which deals with crests and coats of arms and such like things, are full of Lions—Lions in all sorts of attitudes ; with mottoes underneath—the best known being, of course, the royal arms showing " the Lion and the unicorn, fighting for the crown," as the old rhyme says.

South-Eastern Europe once had its Lions, as I have said ; and so much were they feared that they seem to have been hunted and killed out, in one place after another. They probably came from Asia ; and in Asia the Lion is still to be found. But he is far from numerous there, and he is nothing like so grand a beast as his African brother. It is in parts of India and the borders of Persia that he is to be met with chiefly.

Once he abounded in Palestine and Asia Minor, and in these " Bible countries " he seems to have been always regarded as a symbol of all that was powerful, pitiless, and terrible. There are something like one hundred and thirty allusions to Lions in the Bible !

Yet nowadays not one Lion can be met with in those lands. The forests which gave them shelter have mostly been cut down, and even were the Lions to come back to their old haunts they would find that the animals on which they used to prey had grown too few to supply their daily, or rather their nightly, wants.

The tangled thickets that fringe the river Jordan gave cover to the Lion as well as to the leopard, in Bible days ; and when the melting of the mountain snows made the waters of the river rise high above the usual level, and flooded those thickets, the wild creatures that lived or lurked there were driven out into the adjoining country.

That is the meaning of the text in the Book of Jeremiah (ch. xlix. 19), " He shall come up like a lion from the swelling of Jordan."

The man who slew a Lion was looked upon as a benefactor indeed. Usually the slaying was the combined work of a number of shepherds, and a pitfall with sharp spikes at the bottom was the favourite mode of capture.

But now and then some specially strong and intrepid man

would undertake the killing of the fierce beast single-handed. Such a man was Benaiah, the son of Jehoiada, one of David's mighty men. Of him a very bold feat is recorded in the Second Book of Samuel: "He went down and slew a lion in the midst of a pit in time of snow."

Africa, however, is the true home of the Lion. There he reaches his greatest size, there he is seen in all his kingly terrors. There for ages he has been hunted.

A HUNGRY LION.

Once, long long ago, the Pharaohs reckoned Lion-hunting among the royal pastimes; but he is no longer to be found in the land of the Pyramids. In the south of Africa, too, he and his fellows have disappeared from many districts.

Less than two hundred years ago, we are told, the Dutch sentries on the ramparts of Cape Town were quite used to hearing the roaring of Lions as they prowled in the neighbourhood of the little settlement. To-day the British garrison would as little expect to hear a Lion's roar as the people dwelling in a London

9

suburb would expect to hear the howl of a wolf.   In each case it is "a thing of the past."

A recent writer says : "In Cape Colony and the Orange River Colony there is now not a Lion remaining, while in the Transvaal they are only found occasionally here and there in the wild districts of the north and east."   But as we get nearer the heart of Africa we find that Lions are plentiful still.

In the opening sentences of this chapter mention was made of the Lion's reputation for courage.   But during the last quarter of a century some doubts have been cast upon it.   Now and again a hunter has challenged the Lion's right to be called " The King of Beasts," and roundly declared him to be "a cowardly creature who will often slink away rather than show fight."

But most African hunters have a very wholesome respect for the Lion.   They know him to be a foe not lightly to be meddled with.   That great Lion killer, Mr. Selous, has told us that there is no animal in all Africa more dangerous to rouse than the Lion. And although some of those "mighty hunters" whose stories thrill us as we read, talk gaily about their meetings with Lions and the ease with which they shot them, we have to remember that "an old hand" is usually "a cool hand," and some men seem to be born without fear.

The truth, no doubt, is that Lions have often been met with who had no real wish to fight,[1] who, perhaps, had already learned how a rifle-bullet can hurt, and, when next they met a man, had decided that " discretion is the better part of valour," and so had turned tail and fled.   But these are the exceptions.   As a rule, the Lion is a brave foe and a mighty one.   In the words of Mr. H. W. Nevinson : " In spite of all travellers' libels, the Lion is really the king of beasts.   You have only to look at his eye and his forearm to know that."

No country has bred so many bold Lion hunters as our own island.   In modern times, British sportsmen seem to have shown the way in the facing and killing of the king of beasts *single-handed*.   To be one of a hunting party is one thing ; to go forth

---

[1] Herr Schillings says, in his book on sport in Central Africa : "Lions that are not hungry almost always avoid an encounter with men, though, of course, there are exceptions."

A ROYAL PAIR.

[*Drawn by* SCOTT RANKIN.

against him relying solely on your own steady shooting, with no one to " back you up " if you should fail to hit—that is a very different thing.

Even the Boers, capital shots as they have always been, did not believe in tackling a lion single-handed ; they would have thought it was running needless risks.

So, when a Lion had been making himself a nuisance in the neighbourhood, the Boer farmer called together his nearest neighbours, and together they tracked the great beast down, and poured a volley into him.

It wasn't very sportsman-like, but it served its purpose : the prowling foe was got rid of. And it must be said for the Boers that in those old days the country they had settled in was simply infested with Lions, and the big task of clearing them out was done in a very thorough way. Stray Lions still are met with in the Transvaal now and then, but there is no longer " a plague " of them.

But if the Lions have well-nigh disappeared from the two great provinces of the Orange Free State and the Transvaal, which, since the late war, have been British ground, there are other places in Africa where they have proved a pest and a terror even in quite recent years. They are said to be actually on the increase in the province of Angola, and to be getting more dangerous both to the traveller and to his draught-oxen owing to the growing scarcity of the creatures on which they used to depend for their food.

Writing recently of this part of Africa, Mr. Nevinson says : " All the way from Benguela to Bihé you have a good chance of hearing them (Lions) purring about your waggon any night. . . . A native was going down for water in the evening, carrying a petroleum-can, when a Lion sprang on him and split the can with his claw. The boy had the sense to beat his cup hard against the tin, and the monarch of the forest was so disconcerted at the noise that he withdrew. But few natives have so much presence of mind, and many are killed, especially in the mountain region about one hundred miles from the coast."

The same writer adds : " It is very rarely that you have the luck to see a Lion, even where they abound. They are easily hidden. Especially in a country like this, covered with the tawny mounds and pyramids of the white ant, you may easily pass within a few yards of a whole family of Lions without knowing it."

Other travellers have said much the same. Sometimes during the whole of a long expedition the leaders will not sight a single Lion.

During the making of the Uganda Railway the work of laying the line was actually brought to a standstill by two Lions! For three weeks the fierce and crafty creatures so scared the native workers (and there were five thousand of them!), that they threw down their tools and clamoured loudly and piteously to be carried back to the sea-coast by the incoming trains.

The Lions had found out the railway camp, and having pounced on two men with success, they came every night with more and more boldness.

They seemed to bear a charmed life. They were shot at frequently, but the bullets went wide. They were trapped, and got free. They would not touch the poison put temptingly about. Blazing bonfires scare nearly all wild animals, even Lions, but these two giants—they were both nine and a half feet long from nose to tip of tail—thought nothing of the flare and crackle. Once having pulled down a man they went on eating him, while twenty rifle-shots whizzed by them. They sprang over fences and seized men who were huddling in the en-closure. They would stalk in at the door of a labourer's hut or sniff round a crowded tent, and prise up the canvas to see who was inside.

The scare lasted from the month of March 1898 right up to the end of December, when, to the unbounded joy of the whole camp, the two monsters were shot by Mr. J. H. Patterson, the engineer.

In a long and most exciting account of the whole occurrence, Mr. Patterson says: "I sat up almost every night near likely camps, but the Lions either saw me and went elsewhere, or else I was unlucky, for they took man after man without giving me the chance of a shot.

" Matters were getting desperate. As a rule, one Lion would go into a *boma* (enclosure) and do the foraging, but latterly both entered and each seized a man. . . . One night they took a man from the railway station and brought him close to my camp to eat. I could distinctly hear them crunching the bones, and purring like cats over the meal."

The strain on the nerves, to any one watching, gun in hand, in the dark, was terrible. Sometimes the brave engineer would

LIONESS STALKING HER PREY.

[*Drawn by* SCOTT RANKIN.

go to his post alone, and once when he was lying on the top of a staging, staring down at the decoy—the dead body of a donkey— and wishing the Lions would appear, he was nearly startled out of his wits by something striking him on the back of the head. It was—an owl !

Almost before he could recover himself he espied one of the Lions creeping towards the prey. He fired, and the great beast bounded out of sight with a mighty roar, but only to sink down dead. The bullet had gone through the heart.

Says the author of that happy shot: "A tumult of inquiring voices came across the dark jungle from the men in camp, about a quarter of a mile away. On my shouting back that the Lion was dead, such a mighty yell of real joy arose as must have made the wild beasts of the woods around tremble.

"In a short time scores of lamps twinkled through the bushes. Every man in camp turned out and came hurrying towards me, raising a fearful din by playing tom-toms and blowing horns. There was a race as to who should reach me first. I was astonished by their prostrating themselves before me, putting their heads on my feet, and saying 'Mabarak' (which, I believe, means 'blessed one'). . . . We all returned to camp, where there was great rejoicing all night long."

The other Lion continued his nightly visits, and was not killed without the greatest difficulty. One hardly knows which showed the greater pluck—the engineer in following him up after he had been wounded (for what is more formidable than a wounded Lion?), or the Lion itself in coming again and again, and only giving up after six bullets had been lodged in his body.

We often feel grieved when we hear of the slaughter of Lions by modern sportsmen—so piteous does the killing of so magnificent an animal seem to us. But it is when we read descriptions like the above, of the awful mischief a single pair of Lions can do, and the blind terror which seizes the poor helpless natives who have to live in a Lion-infested neighbourhood, that we realise that no pity can be shown them. Whether it is a matter of regret or not, these great fierce beasts of prey must go.

In the old days, when Lions abounded in South Africa, a common practice was for sportsmen to hunt them on horseback, with or without natives and dogs. A well-trained horse or pony would often carry his master to within a few yards of the growling monster, and stand steady while his rider fired: but now and again his very natural terror would get the better of him, and despite bit and spur, he would bolt for safety, sometimes unseating the hunter and flinging him right in the Lion's path.

In Somaliland, too, the native hunters, spear in hand, will

seek out a Lion on horseback.   Occasionally the mettle and speed of the horse is sorely tried, especially when they try to dislodge their quarry from his retreat, and drive him into the open, by setting fire to the grass or brushwood round about the place where they believe him to be lying hidden.   Suddenly with a roar of anger and indignation he will come bounding out, and as his pace for a short distance is surprisingly fleet, the heels and hoofs of the hunting party have all they can do to get out of the way in time.

But in the hot, unhealthy regions of Central Africa, horses cannot thrive, and the hunter has to go afoot, and trust to his own keen eye, steady hand, and deadly weapon.

We usually think of Lions as going about in pairs or singly, but Herr Schillings states that they often roam about in small herds, like the horned creatures they prey upon.   He has himself seen as many as seventeen belonging to one troop, and an English naturalist counted no less than twenty-seven on one occasion.   The big "bag" made by a titled German sportsman, who shot seven Lions one after the other, as they came to feast on the body of a dead elephant, one night, is therefore nothing surprising.

It would seem that Lions often "join forces," the better to secure their prey.   They will mark down a herd of deer, or perhaps zebras (Lions are very partial to zebra flesh), and then approaching the herd from different points they will begin roaring, and so drive the terrified creatures towards each other.

If a Lion can post himself on the high ground overlooking a river or drinking pool, his chances of supper are very good indeed.   From that height he hurls himself in a tremendous spring upon his unsuspecting victim as it stoops to drink.

But even when he has to leap from the same level, the spring is often a prodigious one.   A distance of twenty-four feet was the measurement of one such jump.

As a rule, however, the Lion prefers to *stalk* his prey, and he does so in his own effectual way.   One writer has thus described it : " He creeps up towards it, stretching out his mighty body, and then is upon it like a lightning flash, and kills it with a bite on the back of the neck."

During the day the Lion nearly always retires to his den or some other retreat, and gets his sleep. It is after sun-down that he rises and shakes himself and goes forth to seek and to kill.

No finer picture has ever been drawn, in a few words, of what goes on in a wild country after dark, than is given us, in two or three sentences, by the writer of the hundred and fourth Psalm :

" Thou makest darkness, and it is night; wherein all the beasts of the forest do creep forth. The young lions roar after their prey, and seek their meat from God. The sun ariseth, they gather themselves together, and lay them down in their dens."

It is not only hunger, and the attempt to bewilder their timid prey, that sets the Lions roaring at night. On some of the high tablelands of East Africa the cold at night is severe, and the Lion, especially if he be supperless, does not hide his discomfort as he stalks through the nipping air. Says one who has often heard it : " The tremendous effect of this roaring, as heard in the stillness of the African night, is indescribable."

To the settler of the old days, camped on the veldt with nothing to protect him but his muzzle-loading gun and his crackling watch-fire, the noise must have been dreadfully unnerving. For often a Lion when he roars lays his head to the ground, and the sound rolls out like thunder ; it is difficult then to know exactly in which direction to look for him, and the horrid feeling creeps over a man that the beast may be stealing upon him from a point he least imagines.

The oxen, " out-spanned " from the waggon, grow restive at the sound, and finally, unless very securely tied, they will break loose and rush out into the darkness, quickly to be pounced upon and pulled down.

Many writers, some with knowledge and many with only second-hand knowledge, have written descriptions of the Lion at bay. Some of these accounts are very fanciful. Listen, therefore, to what Mr. Selous says—a writer and hunter who has faced Lions many a time and oft.

" When a Lion stands at bay, he holds his head low down between his shoulders, and, with his eyes fixed on his foe, utters a quick succession of deep grunting roars, twitching his tail all the time from side to side, with little nervous jerks. Should

A FOREST AMBUSH.

[*Drawn by* Cecil Scruby.

he suddenly throw his tail into the air straight and stiff as a bar of iron, then look out, for he means coming."

He adds that, when at bay, a Lion does not snarl like a leopard, but holds his mouth slightly open, while his eyes sparkle and flash "like living fire." "When he charges he does not come with great bounds, but at a heavy gallop, and rushes on, rather than springs on, his prey."

We have seen that when a Lion is angered he can be the most terrible of foes, but it is good to know there is another side to his nature—the side that can be reached by kindness.

Every boy and girl has heard the story of the poor slave, condemned to die in the Roman amphitheatre, and whose life was spared by the Lion who was to have torn him to pieces; and how it was found that the Lion was one which the slave had taken pity on, years before, having drawn from its foot a great thorn which was causing the poor beast much pain.

But most of my readers, I think, will not have heard of the following story about a Lion which was kept, long ago, at the Tower of London.[1]

A certain Mr. Archer, living at the Court of Morocco, had reared a young Lion from cubhood. It used to sleep on his bed, and was playful and gentle to those it knew, but not to strangers.

For some reason or other, Mr. Archer had to return to England, and brought the Lion with him. But, being unable to keep such a big pet in his house, he got permission to house the creature at the Tower. There was no "Zoo" in those days, and sometimes quite a little menagerie was to be seen at the grim old place.

Seven long years went by. Then, one day, there came a party of sightseers, among whom was a man, John Bull, by name, who had been the Lion's keeper when it was a young cub in Morocco.

Now the Lion must have seen thousands of faces in those seven years during which he had been on show; and he had eyed them all with indifference. But no sooner did he catch sight of his old friend than he sprang at the bars with a cry of joy, and began frisking about wildly, purring with delight like a cat.

Bull got leave to go into the cage, and, when he entered, the

---

[1] I told the story some years ago in the *Child's Own Magazine*, and cannot do better than transcribe it.

great beast's joy knew no bounds. It licked his hands and rubbed its head against his knees, and frolicked about till the wondering onlookers thought it was going mad.

When the time came for Bull to go, and he had slipped back through the half-opened door, the Lion was inconsolable. Whining and roaring, it flung itself at the walls of its cage, and for four whole days it would taste no food.

THE HYÆNA.

NO one has any respect for the Hyæna. He is a low, cowardly, sneaking fellow; altogether a disreputable member of the animal world. And he is an unclean beast, too. He is never happier than when he is pulling about the dead body of some other animal, and if it has been dead some days it seems to please him all the more.

Many sportsmen would refuse to spend powder and shot on this prowling miscreant, and I have read somewhere that in those warm, dry lands of South-Western Asia where he abounds the Arabs think even a spear-thrust too good for him, but catch and gag him and hand him over to be stoned to death by the village boys.

And yet with that winged neighbour of his, the vulture, who is equally disgusting in his habits, the much-abused Hyæna does work of the most valuable and necessary kind. He helps to clear the face of the land of those heaps of decaying stuff which under the hot southern sun speedily become putrid, and might easily breed plague.

Nature has specially equipped him for playing the part of scavenger, giving him tremendously strong teeth and jaws, a rough, file-like tongue, a greedy appetite, and a quick digestion. He will make away with the carcase even of a large beast in a very short time, swallowing immense quantities of the often ill-smelling flesh, and crunching up the bones in a way that a veteran wolf might envy; even the thigh-bone of an ox will be split and the marrow extracted. He will tear and burrow his way into a carcase till often he is lost to sight.

Says Herr Schillings, the African traveller : " As darkness drew on, the Hyænas would surround my camp, howling dismally ; they were not in the least afraid of visiting our premises by night to steal flesh or even such things as skins or pieces of leather. . . . Their strength is astonishing. A spotted hyæna can easily run off with an ass." [One of the photographs in his book shows a Hyæna in the act of doing so.]

Böhm, another authority, saw the corpse of a native seized by Hyænas, who "galloped off with it." Schillings found these prowling pests most troublesome on nights that were dark and rainy.

The author of *The Wild Tribes of the Soudan,* writing of the country before Lord Kitchener's conquest, says : " Kassala is rich in Hyænas, chiefly the spotted variety, although we did not find them as numerous as we had done four years before ; then we saw one night fully a hundred quarrelling over the dead body of a donkey. Aylmer's horse died, and we dragged its body out on the sand, some little distance from our tents : we had cause to regret having done so, however, as night was rendered hideous by the frightful noises of these animals. Nothing of the horse was left next morning.

" They are often very bold, and would not only come close to our tents, but one night one of them had the impudence to walk inside while we were in bed. On another occasion, a Hyæna made off with one of a pair of hide sandals that had been left close by the tent door.

" A short time before we arrived in Kassala, a woman and child were killed by one of these creatures as they lay asleep."

It is strange that the Hyæna should not be described, nor even mentioned, in the Bible ; for it is one of the commonest of the larger animals that for ages have prowled and howled in those countries which we call Bible Lands. There is, indeed, a place-name in the Book of Samuel — the Valley of Zeboim — which signifies " the valley of Hyænas." But we should certainly have expected a graphic description of a creature which, although it is a night-walking beast, forces itself on the notice of everybody in the neighbourhood by its unearthly cries.

In these lands—Palestine and Asia Minor especially—it haunts the ancient tombs which the traveller sees scattered about everywhere, especially on the rocky slopes of the hills. Many of these are in ruins, and quite cave-like in their size. They suit the Hyæna exactly. He rather likes the close musty smell of these places, and takes up his abode in them.

So that where, perhaps a thousand years ago, some great personage was laid to rest, and the door of his sepulchre carefully sealed up, now this unclean beast goes in and out at will, bringing in and strewing about the floor of the tomb the bones of sheep and oxen, mules and camels.

The ill-repute of the Hyæna is made worse by its proved liking for human bodies. In its search for such it slinks about grave-

STRIPED HYÆNAS.

yards, and as, in the East, the graves of the poorer folk are very shallow, it finds but little difficulty in digging down with its strong paws. Indeed, even where the grave has been carefully protected with a covering of stones, the horrid robber will dig down sideways and burrow underneath.

Little wonder that the Hyæna is loathed and hated by the people of these lands!

10

Occasionally, but only occasionally, Hyænas will join together and attack a living animal. If it makes a stand and resists vigorously they will often sheer off, like the cowards they are. But if they can scare him into flight they run by his side till he gets weary and panic-stricken, when they leap on him and pull him down. Even the formidable Cape buffalo will lose its life in this way.

There are three species of Hyæna. The one which roams the lands of Scripture is the Striped Hyæna, and it is found also in North Africa, and eastwards to the Himalayas which are the mountain wall of Northern India. The other two kinds, the Brown Hyæna and the Spotted Hyæna, are found in the southern half of the great African continent.

It is the last-named species which is the real Laughing Hyæna. The sounds it utters in the stillness of the African night have a dreadful resemblance to the wild laugh of a person who has gone mad. If the lonely traveller should part the curtains of his tent, and look out to see the cause of the weird cries, he may see the Hyæna going through the strangest antics, excitedly running to and fro, and at times standing on its hind legs, and spinning round like a teetotum, till any one would be positive the animal had itself gone mad.

Hyænas, like vultures, readily shift their quarters and go elsewhere, if there is anything to be gained by it. If plague or war or famine strikes a district, it means a full graveyard, and plenty of dead bodies left lying unburied. The Hyæna folk soon get to know of it, and flock to the place.

But, as a rule, food in plenty is provided for them by the nobler beasts of prey—the lion and the leopard particularly: the " kills " of these great hunters are usually left only partially eaten, and the Hyænas creep up to finish the meal and crack the bones when the killer has gone away.

Modern travellers speak contemptuously of the Hyæna, but when a place is infested with these voracious creatures it is easy to believe that they can become something worse than a nuisance. They are apt, like wolves, to grow bold when they find themselves numerous.

Bruce, the early African traveller, speaks quite seriously

about these pests : " The Hyænas were the scourge of
Abyssinia . . . both of the city and the field ; and they
seemed to surpass even the sheep in number. From evening
till the dawn of day the town of Gondar was full of them.
[They came after the refuse flung out into the streets by the
butchers and others.]

"Many a time in the night, when the king had kept me late in
the palace, on going across the square from the king's house, I
dreaded lest they should bite me in the leg. They grunted in
great numbers around me, although I was attended by several
armed men, who seldom passed a night without wounding or
slaughtering some of them.

"One night I went out of my tent, and returning immediately
I saw two large blue eyes glaring at me in the dark. I called
my servant to bring a light, and we found a Hyæna standing near
the head of the bed. It had two or three large bunches of candles
in its mouth."

Bruce struck at the animal, which thereupon bristled up, and
rushed towards him. It was shot with a pistol, and brained
with " a battle-axe "—a very warlike end for so despicable a
creature. But we must accept Bruce's word for it, when he
winds up his story by saying : " The Hyænas were the plague of
our lives, the terror of our night walks, and the destruction of
our mules and asses, which are their favourite food."

The wounds made by a Hyæna are often terrible. In Africa
natives have been known to have their faces horribly torn, the
nose, and sometimes nose and lips, being bitten off, the cowardly
brute having attacked its victim while he was lying asleep.

In a magazine volume for 1868, I came across an account
of an incident which had taken place during the previous year.

"Mr. Manders, the proprietor of a travelling menagerie,
while he was on the Continent, had purchased a fine pair of
striped Hyænas. These he placed in his Show under the care of
a trusted keeper, Stephen Lawrence.

"One day, while Lawrence was feeding these animals with
some shin-bones of beef, one of them got a piece of bone lodged
in its throat. Seeing that the creature could not dislodge it by
coughing, and thinking that his employer would be greatly

chagrined if the valuable beast was choked, Lawrence opened the door of the cage and stepped inside.

" Seizing the Hyæna by the scruff of its neck, he put his other hand down the animal's throat and drew out the piece of bone. It was a most plucky act, for the jaws of a Hyæna can shut together like a vice.

" The intrusion into their cage did not seem to be resented by either of the Hyænas, and Lawrence henceforth went in and out at any time he pleased, and even trained the two creatures to go through various tricks like other wild beasts.

" But one day, when the Show was at Coggeshall in Essex, at the close of their performance, they attacked the keeper just as he was about to leave the cage. One seized him by the calf of the leg, and the other fastened its teeth into his thigh.

" The crowd watching was much alarmed. One of the audience handed a heavy stick to the keeper through the bars, and he vigorously beat the fierce creatures with it. But they held on, and had soon pulled him down upon the floor of the cage.

" It was not until the proprietor arrived, and thrust back the Hyænas with a big knife hastily strapped to the end of a long pole, that Lawrence was able to rise and crawl out through the door held open for him."

THE JACKAL.

FOR downright impudence the Jackal is hardly to be equalled. Those travellers who make his acquaintance for the first time when he comes to them as a thief and a robber are amazed at the cool audacity of the creature. He is as cunning as his cousin, the fox, and as determined as the wolf. His boldness seems the result of past successes. He has "scored" so often, in his quest for food, that he seems not afraid to poke his sharp nose in anywhere.

He is an unclean little beast, not greatly caring whether the animal flesh he is so busy eating is fresh or tainted. In this he is like his big neighbour, the Hyæna, but somehow he has nothing like so bad a reputation. Despised he may be, but he is not loathed, as the Hyæna of the East is loathed. Indeed, the natives of certain countries do not hesitate to cook and eat him, though when alive there is a very strong, foxy smell about him.

He abounds in those countries which we call Bible Lands, and in many parts of the Bible he is distinctly mentioned, though the old translators have used the word "fox," and even the fanciful word "dragon" instead.

In most cases he is spoken of as an animal that prowled in lonely and waste places—among ruins, for instance. The twenty-second verse of the thirteenth chapter of the Book of Isaiah reads thus, in the New Version: "And wolves [or, howling creatures] shall cry in their castles, and jackals in the pleasant palaces." And the twenty-second verse of the tenth chapter of Jeremiah now reads: "To make the cities of Judah a desolation, a dwelling-place of jackals." While the eighth verse in the first chapter of Micah says: "I will make a wailing like the jackals."

Also in that Old Testament story of Samson's revenge on the Philistines, where we read that he caught a large number of "foxes," and tying firebrands to their bushy tails let them scamper off into the cornfields, it is certain that the word should be " Jackals." It would have taken months to collect so many foxes, whereas Jackals go about in troops, and could easily be taken in snares.

Again, where the Psalmist (Psalm lxiii. 10) declares that his enemies " shall fall by the sword : they shall be a portion for foxes," plainly Jackals are meant. For it is the Jackals that come swarming down to a battlefield, and feast on the bodies of the slain.

Even to-day the natives of those Eastern lands make very little distinction between the fox and the Jackal. And there is plenty of resemblance between the two animals, the golden-brown fur of the Jackal being, however, a good deal lighter than the red-brown of Reynard's coat.

The range of the Jackal is a wide one—right across Asia, and in most parts of Africa, and even in the south-eastern districts of Europe. It is almost everywhere a night prowler. In many places it lurks, fox-like, in the thickets, but in those countries like Palestine, Asia Minor, Persia, which abound in ruins, it has as great a fancy for haunting them as its gruesome friend and fellow-scavenger, the Hyæna.

Canon Tristram, who travelled in the Holy Land in 1863–64, tells how the Jackals used to hang round his camp at night ready to pounce on anything eatable left outside the tents.

When he and his party visited the ruins of Baalbek he found the place infested with these prowlers, the sudden howl of one pack breaking the deep stillness of the desert, only to be answered by the cry of another, till all the air was ringing with their dreary " wailing," and the words of the Old Testament prophecy just quoted (Isaiah xiii. 22) came to his mind with startling force.

The same writer tells how the Jackals came night by night up to the walls of Jerusalem, where the pariah dogs scented them, and howled and barked defiance at these visitors who were even more disreputable than themselves. But woe to the dog who chanced, when alone, to come across a pack of Jackals ; they would soon make an end of him.

A traveller of the present day notes that Jackals, in Africa at all events, do not prowl only in the night-time, though it is then that their wailing is heard. He says: "The Jackals are still on the move in the early morning, hours after the Hyænas have sought their hiding-places." Like the pert little creatures they are, they will not be outdone by any other prowlers in the dark, large or small.

Troops of them range the veldt through the silent hours when the stars are overhead, and they rarely have to go far for food, living or dead. Here they chance upon a crippled antelope, there the huge carcase of an elephant attracts them.

JACKALS ON THE PROWL.　　[*Drawn by* JOSEPH WOLF.

Sometimes they will keep a watch on the movements of some specially active lion or leopard, knowing that there are sure to be pickings—and often a good deal more—where such mighty hunters have been at work.

As soon as he rises from his feast and trots off, the crowd of hangers-on, who have been sitting watching from a discreet distance, rush in to make an end of the torn prey.

Now and then, it would seem, a Jackal's natural impudence

gets the better of his wisdom. He tries to slip in and snap up a piece while the monarch is still feasting. Sometimes he succeeds, but often his impertinence costs him his life. There is an angry flick of the huge paw, and the little intruder is flung back torn and crushed—an object-lesson to his mates, who perhaps had been watching him with envy and interest.

As a rule he finds man a safer provider to steal from. He will prowl round a dwelling, and take up his post close to the very door, so close that he is not noticed when the door is opened. The next instant he has slipped inside, and is making his way to whatever part of the house his keen nose tells him is most worth visiting. Fowls are snatched from their perches, lambs and kids disappear from the fold, and even fat pigs are set upon and made an end of by these voracious thieves.

Sometimes the Jackal finds himself in turn the object of attack : for Jackal-hunting is one of the regular sports of the East.

It is related that on one occasion a couple of greyhounds were after a Jackal, when the 'cute beast turned and made for a neighbouring thicket, giving a sharp signal-cry as he ran. At the sound, a troop of his fellows came rushing out, and fell upon the dogs like little furies, snapping and tearing till the slim hounds were a mass of wounds.

Their master had got stuck in a quagmire, and he and his servants were only able to come to the rescue at the last moment. The hounds were carried home, and it was long before they were able to run again.

As a rule, however, it is the Jackal that gets short shrift. In a book published soon after the late South African War, the author, who served as an officer in Rimington's Guides, tells the following good story of how he chased a Jackal.

" I surprised him about eight o'clock in the morning hanging about the camp. Perhaps he was thinking of making a pounce on the half-dozen scraggy ducks still to be found near the garden dam.

" I had just come off duty, and was mounted on ' Dutchman,' the best of all my ponies. I had a stick with a heavy end to it in my hand. So I gave chase, and when the wily Jackal made for the *kopjes* (rocky hills) I headed him back towards the huge, open

MALE and   MALE.
  FEMALE.

MOUFLON.

flat, five miles long and three miles broad, that stretched between our farm and Bloemfontein.

"After half an hour's galloping, Master Jackal began to slow down . . . and then I clutched my stick, and went full tilt at the flagging beast. Six or seven times he dodged the blow, but at last I got in a heavy crack on his hindquarters. With a snarl of rage he stopped, sat up, and showed fight. This gave me the chance I was looking for, and a couple of blows on the head stunned him.

"At the time I fancied he was dead, and gaily got down and lifted him on to the saddle in front of me. I had only half a mile back to camp, and with one hand clutching his tail and the other his neck, I managed very well for some time.

"But suddenly, to my intense astonishment and alarm, the dead Jackal began to show signs of vigorous life; he grunted, and struggled, and showed his teeth. To add to my difficulties, Dutchman had at once become aware that he was carrying other live stock than myself, and resented the indignity by setting off homeward as fast as he could go.

"There was a *donga* (gully), a *sluit* (dry watercourse), and some torn-down barbed wire fencing between us and the camp; and I could not let go of the Jackal in order to seize the flapping reins; for, if I had, I should either have been bitten or have had to let him go altogether."

So the officer just "sat tight" and rode without reins. He was determined not to lose that Jackal—all the more so because he knew that some forty of his comrades had been watching him, and would have shouted with laughter if the little foxy beast had got away after all.

"On we flew," says the hero of the story; "the louder the Jackal growled, the faster Dutchman galloped. We floundered through the *donga* somehow; we took the *sluit* at a bound; the barbed wire crackled about our legs and fell off again harmlessly; Dutchman reached his well-known peg, and stood still."

A trooper ran up and whipped out his knife, and there was one less Jackal on the South African veldt.

The War, by the bye, did much to scare away many of the more timid wild animals of those great plains, but it is said that

Jackals at once began to increase. Probably this was because the farm-stock which they are too fond of attacking could not be so well guarded in those exciting days, and there was no time to hunt down and kill the four-footed thieves that preyed on them.

Like the fox, the Jackal is not merely an audacious thief: he *thinks*. Some of his reasonings are cleverness itself.

There is a story of a South-African colonist, who found that his fowl-house was being visited nightly by some robber. Not caring to lose his night's rest by sitting up to watch, he fixed a spring-gun in the one opening by which the intruder could reach the fowls. That night the report of the gun roused the excited owner, who hurriedly dressed and went out to the shed. But there was no dead thief to rejoice over ; a thin trail of blood, and a bunch of fur caught in a splintered paling, was all there was to be seen. The fur was clearly that of a Jackal, but the trail of blood could not be traced very far from the house.

Back came the eager searchers, utterly nonplussed. But two days later the thief was found. In some remote place, out on the veldt ? Not a bit of it. In the very heart of the town !

As a matter of fact, the gun-shot had broken the Jackal's leg, and after limping away far enough for the trail to be mixed with other trails, crossing and recrossing it, the 'cute beast had argued to itself that, in its disabled state, to stay out on the veldt would spell starvation.

So, summoning all its impudence to its aid, the creature had boldly run back into the town, and taken up its quarters in a hiding-place close to a butcher's shambles. There it knew it would find food within a few yards, and there it evidently meant to stay until the injured leg was sound again.

WILD SHEEP.

TO any one who has only seen sheep being driven through the streets of our big cities, or crammed into pens in the market-place of a country town, or nibbling grass in an English meadow, they can scarcely seem "kingly" animals.

But I remember one day, some years ago, as I was climbing among the Cumberland hills, I saw a picture which lives in my memory still. I had reached a very lonely spot, high up on the mountain, where the rocks jutted out over what proved to be a steep precipice. Suddenly I looked up, and there on the very crest of the shoulder, standing out sharply against the deep-blue sky, was a magnificent sheep—a horned sheep—with his head erect, motionless, watching me, and with his feet planted on the brink of the precipice.

He took alarm soon enough, and bounded away out of sight, but I had seen a picture that I often recall—a sheep that was truly a kingly animal.

I have an idea that he was one of the Highland breed of sheep, for he had the fine curly horns of that branch of the family, but whatever he was, in truth he was a splendid fellow.

And yet, even he could not compare for a moment with the real kings of his tribe—the Wild Sheep that roam free on the mountainside in other parts of the world, and never answer the shepherd's call. It is about one or two of these that I want to say something. Let me begin with the one nearest home.

THE MOUFLON.

Naturalists seem to have grouped quite a number of Wild Sheep of different sorts and countries under this name:

but we are meaning here the Mouflon which belongs to Europe.

He is found chiefly among the mountains of Corsica and Sardinia, and is worthy of any sportsman. In the former island, the numbers are getting so low that, unless care is taken to protect him from the gun, he is likely ere long to be seen no more there.

But in Sardinia there are plenty of Mouflons, however difficult they may be to capture or kill. Indeed, often you will not see a single one. For they have a habit of taking shelter in the tall, heathery undergrowth which clothes the mountains, as soon as they scent danger. This heather is so dense that the sportsman cannot easily follow them. Moreover, during the long, hot summer days at least, they keep quiet in their retreats, coming out to feed only at dark.

The hunter has a better chance of coming across them in the late autumn, when they move about more freely. The sheep pastured on the higher slopes during summer have then been driven down to the valleys, and the Mouflon finds himself in undisturbed possession of his favourite feeding-grounds. He grows bolder, and less suspicious. Then is the hunter's chance.

The Mouflon is a creature worth taking any trouble to stalk. He stands between two and two and a half feet high at the shoulder, and the male animal, with his great horns curling round till they almost meet upon his neck, and his brown coat with white markings, is a very handsome fellow indeed.

THE ARGALI.

He is the kingliest of all the Wild Sheep. Think of it—a sheep often known to measure three feet six to four feet in height at the shoulder, with a pair of magnificent wrinkled horns, sometimes as much as nineteen inches round,

HUNTING THE ARGALI.

"TO HIS ASTONISHMENT HE SAW THE WHOLE FLOCK RUSHING TOWARDS HIM."

at the root, and four feet in length if they could be straightened out ; and with the alert · step and sharp eyes of a mountaineer.

He must be sought for in Asia—mid-Asia ; in such countries as Southern Siberia, and Northern Mongolia, and the long unknown land of Thibet.

When you look at those enormous horns you wonder that they do not weigh him down and overbalance him as he makes his way along some snowy ledge or narrow shelf among the mountains. Even more so, perhaps, when in some desperate battle with a rival one of the horns is snapped off. But whether it be on icy slope or loose, rough stones, the Argali seems able to look after himself perfectly well.

If he is scared while grazing in the lower valleys, temptingly green after the barren heights on which he lives, he makes for the high ground, as if by instinct. A steep or difficult slope is nothing to an Argali when danger is at his heels.

Here is an account of an Argali hunt in the land of the Turcomans. It is from a French book of travel written some years ago. Says the author, who was a keen sportsman :

" I set off at daybreak with the khan (chief), two huntsmen, and Chaban. We took our way at once towards the Tek-Biran Mountains. Our horses carried us as far as the encampment of some Kurd shepherds, in whose care we left them. Then we scrambled slowly and painfully, almost on our hands and knees, up the steep rocks that rose before us.

" In places where the sun had melted the snow, the Argalis were feeding. Our huntsmen were not long in announcing a flock. Like the chamois, the Argalis station sentinels, so that the rest of the flock may browse without any danger of being taken by surprise.

" Half an hour was enough to bring us within firing distance of the game. Before us rose a very high rock. We clambered up it, and the sight that met our eyes made us forget all our fatigue.

" On the opposite side of the ravine were gathered thirty Wild Sheep ; the rams easily to be recognised by their great twisted horns, their necks and breast being covered with a heavy mane.

The young ones, with short, straight horns, were browsing fearlessly.

"I was admiring the beautiful picture they made, when I felt the khan, who was just behind me, pull my sleeve, whilst he whispered '*Argali*,' and then pointed to a big sheep which had approached, all unsuspecting, within fifty feet of us."

The writer fired, and, when the rifle smoke had cleared away, to his astonishment he saw the whole flock rushing towards him. The report of the gun, it seems, had raised echoes which quite bewildered the flock, and sent it flying into the very teeth of danger.

With a rush they scampered past the party of hunters, who were too surprised to take proper aim. But the dead Argali was soon found. His horns were marked with twelve rings (a twelve-year-old), and he weighed nearly two hundred-weight.

"The native hunters only carry home the best portions of the carcase; the horns and the rest are always left behind on the mountain. But as I wanted to have a specimen of an Argali properly stuffed, I had brought one of the shepherds, and he undertook to carry the prize home to my comfortable quarters."

THE BIG-HORN.

The American sportsman need not leave his own country if he wants a spell of Wild Sheep hunting. For the Big-horn is to Canada and the United States what the Argali is to Central Asia, and the Mouflon to Europe.

His horns are not quite so wrinkled, and he himself may perhaps be slightly less tall, but there is little to choose between him and his Asiatic cousin.

He is a most shy creature, and during the last fifty years his race has been so often shot at that it takes a mere trifle to send him galloping up the mountain path to his citadel among the high crags.

There he loves best to wander, always on the watch against surprises, and finding food enough in the small patches of green grass that grow in sheltered nooks even there.

Now and then in winter a heavier fall of snow than usual will oblige him to seek food lower down the mountain, but he goes warily, and is not quite happy till he is back again among his rocky home surroundings.

The earlier miners and settlers in California found the Big-horn suspicious but bold, staring at the in-

STALKING A BIG-HORN.

truders that came near his retreat. But the sight or scent of a man nowadays is quite enough to disperse a herd of them, the alarm being given by the peculiar whistling note of the sentries.

The " range " of the Big-horn is a wide one—from Mexico in the south to Alaska in the north.

GNUS.

TO call a Gnu an antelope seems as absurd as it would be to say that a zebra is a kind of deer. Yet naturalists insist that he *is* a member—a very odd-looking member, if you like—of the great antelope family. And certainly where most of the members of that very big clan have their home, there is the Gnu.

At first sight, as they go tearing across the dry plains of Africa in a dust-storm of their own raising, a herd of Gnus might almost be taken for a troop of frolicsome horses ; or, to judge by their heads, a herd of slimly built " buffaloes " of the old North American prairie sort. For they lower their heads as they gallop, ducking them between their forefeet in true bison style, and they have queer horns that bend outward and upward in rather an odd way, and a lot of thick hair about the neck and throat and face.

There are two other kinds of Gnu to be found on the African plains, but the Brindled Gnu is the most curious in appearance. The White-tailed Gnu, which is otherwise brown in colour, is merely strange-looking by reason of its very broad nose ; and the powerfully built White-bearded Gnu, which lives rather in the East than in the South of Africa, is chiefly noticeable for its formidable horns that branch out like those of an ox.

The Boers gave the Gnu the name of Wildebeest or Wild Ox. Gordon Cumming has a good description of these animals. He noticed how they behaved when they espied anything which roused their suspicion or their anger : " They commence whisking their long tails . . . then, springing suddenly into the air, they begin pawing and capering, and pursue each other in circles at their utmost speed. Suddenly they all pull up together to deal with the intruder, when some of the bulls [male Gnus] will often begin fighting in the most violent manner, dropping on their knees at every shock ; then, quickly wheeling about, they kick

A STAMPEDE OF GNUS AND ZEBRAS.

[*Drawn* by W. THOS. SMITH.

up their heels, whirl their tails with a flourish, and scour across
the plains, half-hidden in a cloud of dust."

They are constantly found in company with zebras, with whom
they will roam far and wide, and the dust thrown up when a
stampede of these strong, swift animals occurs may be easily
imagined.

Often a number of ostriches and a few gazelles will be seen

WHITE-TAILED GNU.

feeding with the Gnus and zebras—strangely assorted comrades,
it seems to us, but all of them fleet of foot, should danger threaten.
Another characteristic that Gnus and zebras have in common is
that of being able to go for a long time on water that is brackish
or even briny.

In the less-trodden parts of East Africa, Gnus will let the hunter
approach fairly near before taking alarm. But, as a rule, the

sight of anything that seems to spell danger sets them scampering for their lives. Very often, though, after they have gone some distance, they stop and wheel round, and stare back at the person or thing which put them to flight. They begin to wonder what it was. Then their curiosity gets the better of their prudence. They come back, and gallop round and round the cause of their alarm.

Hunters early learnt to take advantage of this inquisitiveness. They would hoist a hat or a handkerchief on the end of a rifle, and the Gnus would be unable to resist the wish to come back and see what the strange object might be. When once they had come within range, of course the hat or the handkerchief suddenly disappeared, and the deadly rifle-shot laid low the best of the herd.

It was found almost impossible to come up with a Gnu on horseback, for it took fright so quickly, and could keep up its gallop for such a long time. Yet, unlike the bison of the prairies, it seldom turned on its pursuer unless cornered, though it has a most formidable weapon in its horns, and it can easily toss a man when it is angered.

All it asks for is liberty—the liberty of the boundless, sun-scorched plains of its African home.

Specimens of the Gnu have been brought to Europe, to the Zoo in London and elsewhere. But it loses its temper in confinement, and becomes quite dangerous even to its attendants.

One of the most singular ways in which a Gnu was captured is related by the hunter, Gordon Cumming, to whom I have just referred. He noticed a Gnu running somewhat slowly and clumsily, and on coming up with it he found that it had managed —very likely in fighting one of its fellows—to get one of its front legs over its horn, and was unable to draw it back. The trick which a Gnu has of charging with its head between its forefeet makes this easy to understand.

In his beautifully produced book, *A Breath from the Veldt*, Captain Millais gives a most lively description of the Gnus he had seen in South Africa. He has a high opinion of their reckless courage, and tells how " a Wildebeest (Gnu) with her young calf was pursued by three Cape wild dogs—creatures as daring and persistent as the red dogs of India. She killed two, and the third was shot by a hunter, with whom the Wildebeest at once prepared to do battle."

It is grievous to think of the way this curious animal is disappearing from the plains where it once roamed in countless numbers. Of the White-bearded Gnu a good many are still to be seen in East Africa, but of the White-tailed Gnu few, if any, survive, except in a preserved state.

Even before the late South African War broke out, Mr. Selous knew of only two herds remaining in the Transvaal and what is now the Orange River Colony. One was left in its wild state, but preserved from molestation by the old Boer, Piet Terblaus, on whose extensive farm, near Kronstadt, these strange creatures led their roving life.

It might well be expected that the coming of the railway would scare Gnus and all other "game" to a great distance. Yet we are told that when the Uganda Railway was built plenty of wild animals that had been scared away by the noise of the workmen engaged in making the line, came back to the railroad, not in the least perturbed by the shining track of parallel steel bars driven through their old solitudes.

Lions, elephants, and other creatures of a less lordly kind paid it a visit. And one of the most striking sights seen from the train—and happily photographed—was a long string of brindled Gnus on the march. They moved in single file across the open veldt, in line with the railway, never turning aside when a train rattled by. The loosely strung-out procession was reckoned to have been nearly four miles in length.

SOME OF THE ANTELOPES.

THE ELAND.

HE is a very fine fellow indeed, and of all the large family of African antelopes he is undeniably the chief member, if size and strength are to count. His height varies from five to six feet at the shoulder, and thanks to the amount of fat with which his chest and shoulders are padded, he often weighs not far short of a ton.

Most of the antelope tribe are swift runners, but the Eland is easily overtaken by a well-horsed hunter.

One who has often been out after these animals says that on seeing or scenting danger the whole herd stop feeding and begin rushing together ; then they take to flight, first at a trot, then at a gallop. But the oddest part of it is that although they run so heavily, they go through a series of high jumps which seem quite unnecessary, and certainly are most unexpected in such massive creatures.

Also they can make their way up a mountain side in the most active fashion, and in East Africa they have been found wandering many thousands of feet above the sea-level. They seem to quit the plains in the dry season when the veldt is scorched up, and move up to "green pastures" on the mountains. Of course, in parts of South Africa there are no such green retreats to climb to, but the herds appear to wander great distances when food grows scarce.

The Eland is very easily distinguished from other antelopes by its long body, the hump on the shoulders, the hanging folds of the neck,—the dewlap, as it is called,—and its straight-pointing, spirally-twisted horns, which often measure from twenty-six to thirty-three inches in length.

Eland meat is much sought after ; and the flesh of the young Eland, when well fed, during the rainy season, is said to be delicious. But even when the grass and herbage are almost like tinder, these great creatures manage to get nourishment out of it ; and at any time they can go without water for several days.

Attempts have been made to find out whether the Eland

ELAND, AT THE ZOOLOGICAL GARDENS.

would live out of doors in England. It was hoped that, in that case, the big creature might be added to the list of animals used for food. Some say that the variableness of our climate would be against such a thing, and that it is only at places like the Zoo, where they can have warmth and cosy quarters whenever they need them, that they would thrive in this country. Yet in several lordly parks herds of them have been kept, as far back as fifty years ago, and there are experts who say that the Eland might easily be acclimatised.

———◆———

THE KUDU.

If the Eland is the largest of the antelope family, the Kudu is certainly the most splendid looking. Even in height he runs his heavily built relative very close, and he can jump with an agility that would do credit to a springbuck. Altogether the Greater Kudu (for there are two Kudus, the Greater and the Lesser) is a very fine creature indeed.

Nor is that all the good that can be said of him. He is a quiet-loving, peaceable animal. Even when he is attacked by dogs his temper is not roused, and instead of turning on them as a stag would, with flashing eyes and lowered head, he will allow himself to be pulled down if he cannot escape by flight. Yet it is not for want of power to defend himself. Those fleet hoofs could easily kill or maim any of his yelping foes, and his long twisted horns could inflict terrible wounds.

Young Kudus captured and tamed have proved, we are told by one writer, "gentle, playful, and affectionate," showing, too, "strong attachment to their owner."

The colour of the Kudu varies from light brown to dark grey, and several white stripes, sometimes four, sometimes as many as eight, run down the sides and flanks. These stripes, like the stripes of the zebra, help to conceal him, by making him hard to distinguish from the bushes and grass, streaked as these are with light and shadow. His throat and chest are clothed with a mass of long hair which hangs down in reindeer fashion. His ears are large and rounded, and are always moving this way and that to catch the faintest sound that spells danger: they are sentinels that serve him well.

But it is the horns that one notices chiefly, in a male Kudu. They are often magnificent, measuring as much as three and a half feet even in a straight line ; but they curve and twist corkscrew-wise, and would measure nearly five feet if they could be straightened out.

As the Kudu is a lover of wooded country, one would fancy that such horns would prove what his long hair was to the young Prince Absalom in the Bible story—a glory to him, but eventually the cause of his death. Rushing timidly through the trees and bushes it would seem difficult to avoid getting those twisting, upstanding horns entangled.

But of that danger, as of others, the Kudu seems to be well aware ; and so when he runs he lays his horns well back on his neck, deer-wise, and slips safely through the difficult bush. The females of the herd have no horns.

Wooded hills are the favourite home of the Kudu, and if they be found on the plains there is pretty certain to be plenty of bush, and water within easy distance. Grass may be their chief food, but they love leaves and wild fruit as well.

Mr. Selous says the Kudus —in South Africa, at all events—seldom go about in

AN ANTELOPE FAWN.

large herds ; twenty or thirty is the usual number, but there are often only half as many. Of late years, too, the Kudu has disappeared from certain districts. Many have fallen to the rifle, of course, but more destructive by far has been that terrible plague, the rinderpest, which, towards the end of last century, laid low countless thousands of the beautiful wild creatures that roamed over the southern half of the great African continent. Mr. Selous states that the Kudu and the Cape buffalo suffered worse than the other animals ; the havoc made by the disease was simply awful, and many places where this magnificent antelope could always be found will see its soft eyes and noble horns no more.

The flesh of the Kudu is said to be particularly good eating, and the African Bushmen used to have their own way of securing such savoury food.

A party of them would search till they found the spoor (footprints) of a Kudu, and follow the tracks till they came in sight of him. He was up and off at once, of course, but the pursuit was kept up, one man running fast, the others more slowly, and each in turn relieving the foremost runner.

It was hot work and thirsty, and there would usually be several women carrying ostrich egg-shells filled with water to refresh the runners. The chase would last many hours, and was rarely abandoned until the poor Kudu, who dared not rest for more than a few minutes, sank down utterly tired out.

The skin is much prized, whip-lashes, harness, and other articles being made from it.

The Lesser Kudu is not such an imposing animal—not so tall, with shorter horns, and with no long fringes of hair along the throat. It is found in Somaliland and along the coast region of British East Africa. It may easily escape the notice of the traveller, for by day it usually lies hid in the thick scrub. He and his little knot of companions—the Lesser Kudu never go about in big herds—come out

"When the blazing sun is gone,"

and browse on the leaves of their favourite trees. Occasionally they are seen feeding in the early morning, but they are very hard to approach, though sometimes they may pretend not to see the hunter until he is dangerously close. Says one who has tried to stalk them: "Often they will allow you to come right up to them, and then, taking to flight, make off at a tremendous pace, and you will never see them again."

———◆———

THE SPRINGBUCK.

"When all things were made, none was made better than the Springbuck. He is among deer and antelope what the greyhound is among dogs—the lithest, slimmest, fleetest of his race."

Thus does one writer, who served as a soldier in the South African War, sing the praises of the little animal he had so often watched, and had sometimes chased when he had a good horse under him.

Of the antelopes we have just been considering two can scarcely be called true specimens of their tribe: the Eland is too heavy and

ANTELOPES AND OSTRICHES—A SCENE ON THE VELDT.

ox-like, and the Gnu, as we have seen, is more like a buffalo-headed horse. But the Springbuck is an antelope out and out.

In the first place, it has wonderful agility and speed, and that is above all things characteristic of this numerous and beautiful class of animals. Indeed, its name speaks for it. It was so called because the moment this alert, quick creature is scared by anything it is off and away with leaps and bounds, which are astonishing to any one who watches it.

If it fancies itself pursued, its even pace will be broken by high leaps into the air ; its legs well tucked under it, and its back sharply hunched ; and fleet, indeed, would be the horse that could keep it long in view. Some of the jumps are as much as seven, eight, and even twelve feet in height.

It is a most timid little animal, and rarely allows man to come within easy distance of it. Yet, if the traveller's waggon has been halting during the night near their feeding-grounds, Springbuck will draw near, made unsuspicious by its quietness, or deceived by the darkness. A very pretty word-picture of such a scene appeared, some years ago, in the *Cape Magazine*, drawn by a lady from her own experience :

" Early, just as the day is breaking, you wake, and, lifting the flap of the waggon, look out at the coming morning. To your entire surprise you see a little group of five or six Spring-bucks that have been sleeping not more than two hundred yards from the waggon. They are just getting up, stretching them-selves lazily and giving queer little coughs, ' phrumph ! phrumph ! ' as they move slowly away, feeding as they go. So graceful they look, with their beautiful heads, smooth skins, and long slender legs. Suddenly something startles them, and they dash away through the bushes."

It is good to learn that the Springbuck is not in danger of being slaughtered out, like so many of the fleet and beautiful creatures that once thronged the wide plains of Southern Africa. Measures have been taken to protect it, and to-day it is far from uncommon there. Indeed, it is numerous enough to cause much anxiety to the farmers of Cape Colony over whose grazing grounds it will pass now and then in great herds, nibbling the grass to the roots.

For, like the Boer farmers of former days, the Spring-buck are accustomed to *trek* ; they remove to new districts many miles away. The Boers long ago noticed this, and called these restless animals " trek-bokken," or travelling-bucks.

In those old days when the sportsman's gun had not done much to thin the numbers of South African game, the trekking was a very big business indeed. One old-time hunter describes

THE SPRINGBUCK.

what he saw once in the early morning, as he peeped out from his waggon :—

" Looking about me I beheld the ground to the northward of my camp actually covered with a dense living mass of Spring-bucks, marching slowly and steadily along, from an opening in a long range of hills on the west, through which they con-tinued pouring like the flood of some great river." He remained watching them for two hours, by which time the last of the countless horde had disappeared over a ridge in the distance.

The strangest stories—strange but true—are told of these treks. Sometimes the herd of Springbucks happens to move over a part of the plain where sheep or goats are feeding, and the living tide catches them up and sweeps them onward. There is no resisting such a crowd, and, until the herd breaks up and disperses a little, there is no escape. Even lions have been known to get surrounded by these travelling herds, and been hustled into moving along with the very animals they would fain have eaten— a truly undignified position for the King of Beasts.

But if the lion or leopard takes care to keep well outside the moving mass he is likely to have as much food as he desires. He has only to watch and wait until some tired or sick member of the army lags and wanders clear of the pushing, pressing bodies behind it. Then with a bound he can be upon it, and devour it at leisure.

Indeed, though in one sense the herd forms a solid mass, it is continually shifting within itself. For as the antelopes in front are the first to reach the new pasture, so they are satisfied first, and having eaten their fill, they " fall back," like soldiers changing rank, and those behind step to the front. Thus all of them in turn get their share of the good green grass.

Livingstone saw something of these antelope treks and wondered what it was that drove them to travel thus. In his day it was thought that they were in search of water. But it would appear that they come after the young fresh grass which springs so quickly in Africa after the dry season has broken up, and the abundant rains have fallen.

This short green growth just suits the Springbucks, for they dislike feeding on the long upstanding grass which grows tall

12

enough to hide them, horns and all.   They know that in such grass there are likely to be enemies lurking, ready to spring.

The South African War meant trouble for the Springbucks as for every other dweller on the veldt.   The writer of a delightful series of letters, since printed, says that " the Battle of Driefontein raged over a large herd of Springbuck, which circled round and round, trying vainly to break through the hordes (of soldiers) that hemmed them in.   Pitiable was their terror as shells hurtled over them and bullets sang about their ears. One poor wounded beast came limping up alone to within a hundred yards of where I lay."

The Springbuck is closely related to the Gazelles, about which something must now be said.

---◆---

THE GAZELLES.

There are many of them, each with its own distinctive name, and they are all beautiful.   Some of the smaller ones seem to have wandered out of fairyland, so slight and slender and graceful are they.   But beauty " runs in the family "—one cannot even imagine a clumsy Gazelle.

From earliest times the little creature has been a type of all that is light-footed and swift and dainty.   Poets compared the eyes of beautiful women to those of a Gazelle—Arab singers do so nowadays—and the word was even used as a girl's name.

There are plenty of references to this animal in the books of the Old Testament, though the Hebrew word has wrongly been translated "roe."   Asahel, the brother of Joab, David's general, was " light of foot as a wild gazelle."   Some of the men who flocked to David in the wilderness are described as being " swift as the gazelles upon the mountains."   And in the Song of Solomon we have the words, " Behold, he cometh leaping upon the mountains, skipping upon the hills . . . like a gazelle or a young hart."   The Arab word for it is *Ghazal*, from which, of course, our word comes.

The Gazelle is one of the commonest wild animals of Scripture lands even now, though, no doubt, with the coming of railways and the bustle of civilisation it will be scared away from many places where it used often to be seen.

Forty years ago Canon Tristram could write thus :

"Small herds of Gazelle are to be found in every part of the country (*i.e.* Palestine); and in the south they congregate in herds of nearly a hundred together. . . . Though generally

GAZELLES.

[Drawn by JOSEPH WOLF.

considered an animal of the desert and the plains, the Gazelle appears at home everywhere. It shares the rocks of En-gedi with the wild goats ; it dashes over the wide expanse of the desert beyond Beersheba. We found it in the glades of Carmel, and it often springs from its leafy covert on the back of Tabor, and screens itself under the thorn-bushes of Gennesaret. . . . And I have seen a little troop of Gazelle feeding on the Mount of Olives, close to Jerusalem itself."

A later traveller also says: "One was killed within a mile

of Jerusalem in heavy snow, and brought into my hotel during my stay there." But this cannot be said to be likely to happen nowadays — tourist parties are too many, and the coming and going would scare a less wild creature than the Gazelle.

Where there is plenty of cover the traveller may often come unexpectedly upon a pair or even a small herd of these nimble-footed " desert rangers," but in the south of Palestine and the dry waste wildernesses of Arabia and Sinai, where anything moving can be seen from a great distance, they usually espy before they are espied, and are off like the wind.

The Arabs are fond of Gazelle venison, and use their old-fashioned guns with some effect. But the favourite way of hunting the Gazelle is, or was until recently, the very picturesque way of using " hawk and hound."

The Arab — usually a sheikh or chief — would ride out accompanied by his dog, a greyhound of Persian breed " with long silky ears and silky tail," and carrying on his wrist a trained falcon. As soon as a herd of Gazelle was sighted, the falcon was unhooded and thrown off, and immediately soared up into the air and sailed straight for the quarry.

Then it was a race between fleet hoofs and fleet wings, and the wings usually won. Coming up with the Gazelle as it clattered madly over the loose stones of the hillside, the falcon swooped down upon its head, and with claws and wings so checked its speed that the hound which had been following with long bounds was able to come up and pull down the panting creature.

Now and then it happened that the falcon was too much in a hurry, and, in swooping down, impaled itself on the sharp dagger-like horns. In such cases the Gazelle usually succeeded in making its escape.

Talking of a Gazelle's horns, I may say here that peaceful and timid though the little creature is known to be, it is quite aware of this pair of weapons in its head.

A recent African traveller relates how he shot at a Gazelle " with a pair of stately horns with very sharp points." She was on a hill, and when hit she came running down and made for him, bleating loudly.

He was amazed at her boldness, but suddenly guessed that her young must be hidden in the grass somewhere close by. The wound had roused all the mother's courage, and she would undoubtedly have charged the hunter, and wounded, possibly killed him, had not his second shot taken effect when she had got within a few yards of him.

But it is not only in moments of boldness that a Gazelle will use its horns. It is quite customary for a herd to unite together against a common foe—say, an attack by jackals. Quickly the young ones and the females are gathered into the centre of the herd, and the males stand round in a close circle, with their sharp horns turned towards their barking, snapping enemy.

Of course, in the case of such foes as the mighty lion or the lithe sinewy leopard the only safe course is to take to flight without an instant's delay.

When feeding, a herd always posts its sentinels. These watch with eyes and ears and nostrils, and give the alarm the moment danger approaches. Then away goes the whole troop, with light bounding feet that mock the hunter, be he man or beast, who thought to stalk them.

The Gazelle has a very wide range. It is found, as we have already seen, in Western Asia, and members of the clan live in Persia, Thibet, Mongolia, and India. In Africa it is more or less common from Senegal to the Red Sea, and from Algeria to Somaliland.

PET GAZELLE, AT A HINDU ANIMAL HOSPITAL.

Year by year the changes wrought even in Africa by war and trade scare the Gazelle from places where once it was abundant.

For example, Mr. F. L. James, in his book *The Wild Tribes of the Soudan,* says of the country between Suakim and Berber: " We saw a few Gazelle, but all very shy. Each year they become less numerous on the caravan routes ; and my brother said that they were far less common than when he passed over the same road four years before." And this was as far back as 1878, since which the locomotive has come snorting into the silent wastes of the Soudan !

THE CAMEL.

WHEN I was a little boy I used to wonder who first tamed the Camel, and where did that first tame Camel come from.

In the oldest histories, even in the early chapters of the Book of Genesis, I noticed that the animal was always spoken of as in man's service ; there was no mention of wild Camels. Yet the first tamed Camels must have been captured from a wild herd. How was it, then, that we heard little or nothing of Camels that lived in a wild state ?

The answer seems to be that man had his eye upon the Camel, as a useful helper to carry his loads, from a very early time indeed —perhaps before even Egyptian history began to be written. The long-legged, long-necked, pad-footed creature was not fleet enough to avoid capture, like the wild ass ; nor was he too formidable to tackle. Very likely, too, his captors caught him while he was young and fairly docile.

Naturalists think they have found the true wild Camel— wild still—on the dry, wind-swept plain of Tsaidam, in Central Asia. The Camel there is a healthy, hard-living beast, and able to endure much that would kill his tame relatives in the sunnier lands to the south.

About these northern Camels I shall have something to say later on.

———◆———

THE ARABIAN CAMEL.

The Camel gets his name from the Hebrew language, and the word (*Gamal*) has been taken over with very little alteration by other peoples—Greeks, Arabs, etc.

So we need not be surprised to find constant references to this animal in the Old Testament, which is so largely a history of the Hebrew nation from its earliest beginnings. Camels are among the presents given to Abram by the king of Egypt, and by Jacob to his angry brother Esau. Joseph is drawn up from the pit into which he had been cast by his jealous brethren, and sold to a passing caravan of Ishmaelites, who came by " with their camels bearing spicery, and balm, and myrrh, going to carry it down to Egypt."

Later on, in the days of the Judges, there was an invasion of the land of Israel by the Midianites and the Amalekites, of whom we are told, " their camels were without number, as the sand by the seaside for multitude." Again, in what we may call a border raid by Amalekites in David's day, we find that warrior hero swooping down upon the party of plunderers while they were feasting and exulting over their spoils, not one of them escaping except " four hundred young men who rode upon camels."

The long, swinging stride of this desert steed must have carried many a defeated fighter safely out of the battle, in ancient days. But where horses were used even his long legs were outmatched ; as when, for instance, Zenobia, the warlike queen of Palmyra, fled from the victorious Romans. Her city having been taken, she mounted her swift camel, and hurried off across the desert sands. But a troop of Roman cavalry espied her and gave chase, and the galloping horses easily came up with the " dromedary," and she was made captive.

But the Camel can live in places where the horse would soon flag and collapse. Even in these modern times, when man gets what he needs from all over the world, he has found no animal that can take the place of the Camel for expeditions across desert places.

So, when General Gordon was besieged in Khartoum, and an army was sent out from England to rescue him, the greater part of the expedition went all the way by river, *i.e.* up the Nile in boats, but a picked force of some twelve hundred men were mounted on Camels, and took the short cut across the Bayuda Desert.[1]

[1] In his book *With the Camel Corps up the Nile*, Count Gleichen, one of the officers of the corps, says of this journey : "It was a new and pleasant sensation, riding ahead of the

And even in far-away Australia, Camels, brought from India most likely, were found of the greatest use as carriers in the brave attempts made to cross the burning deserts, and find out what was at the heart of that island-continent. The heat was fearful, water was very scarce and often not to be found, and only the

ARAB AND HIS CAMEL MOUNT.

patient, plodding Camels could have carried a pack across that sun-baked wilderness.

Look well at a Camel and notice how extraordinarily well-formed he is for his work and his surroundings. Notice his broad, splay feet with their leather-like pads—just the very " tread " for the loose, dry sands of the desert, into which a sharp, hard hoof would sink at every step.

Look, too, at the parts of his body which come against the rough ground when he stops to rest or to receive his load—the knees and the breast; both are protected by pad-like shields. And for burden-bearing, what could be better than that mound-like hump, which can uphold a weight of five or six hundred pounds ?

Last, but not least, that useful stomach of his, which can store as much as five or six quarts of water, and draw upon this supply day by day. This little reservoir enables him to get good from, and even to relish, the dry, tasteless thorn-bushes and scrubby herbage, which is the only food that grows in those desert regions

column in the quiet moonlit desert, not a sound being made by the two thousand Camels in rear, as their padded feet passed over the sand. By and by the men got sleepy, and their laughter and talking grew fainter and fainter, till at last it ceased altogether."

—just as to you, when you are thirsty, a dry biscuit is always more pleasant and easy to eat when you have something to drink with it.

Altogether the Camel is a hard-living animal. His fare is hard, his training is hard, and his whole life, after his baby days are past, is one of hard work and hard usage. His owner, if he be a sensible and intelligent man, takes care of him, and treats him as a good master should treat a useful servant, but he never cares for him with that affectionate interest often felt by a man for his horse. And too frequently the treatment is harsh, nay, downright cruel—as cruel as the way the London costers fifty years ago used to treat their donkeys.

One writer and traveller, Dr. Robinson, describing the strange and piteous noises made by these animals while their loads are being strapped on, says: "The Arabs heed not their cries, nor does the poor animal find much mercy at their hands. Heavy and galling loads and meagre fare are his portion, and God has hardened him to them."

Whether hard treatment has soured the temper of the Camel, or whether his bad temper has provoked the harsh usage, it is difficult to say; but the two things seem to go together, unhappily, far too often.

It cannot be denied that of all beasts of burden he is one of the worst-tempered. Here is a picture of him by one who had good reason to remember his "tantrums": "Watch him when he is being loaded; see his keeper struggling frantically with him, only succeeding by sheer force in making him kneel down, and when down, only keeping him there by tying neck and fore-legs together tightly with a piece of string. Hear him grumbling in deep, bubbling tones, with mouth savagely opened."

And when at last the loading is completed, and his bonds are loosened, up he rises, a great brown mountain, still groaning, still bubbling, and away he goes, madly dashing to and fro, and shaking off tables, portmanteaux, beds, furniture, and baggage in a scattered shower around him.

The training of a Camel is not a pleasant task. His temper can never be trusted, and he is often as spiteful as a zebra. Moreover, he is an extremely stupid animal. If he strays ever so little he loses himself completely; if he finds himself in danger of drowning, he makes no struggle for life, but gives himself up in the most pig-headed, helpless way imaginable.

What with his stupidity and his bad temper, his trainers lose patience and are severe and unfair to him. They jump to the conclusion that the stick, the heavy stick and nothing but the stick, will teach him to obey. And so the stick is laid on without stint. The new Camel, though his skin is pretty tough, roars defiantly, then piteously, then sullenly, and at last he submits.

But all his life the Camel is a rebel, though " a rebel in chains." He never learns, like the horse—especially the Arab horse—to love his master. So his master and his master's servants do well to be always on their guard. At any moment, if angered, he may lash out with his great feet, or snap with his ugly mouth.

A less serious habit, though a very unpleasant one, is that of turning his long neck, glaring at his rider, and spitting in his face.

Many stories are told of the Camel's spitefulness. Here is one. A boy of fourteen was given the charge of a big Camel loaded with wood. It was in the plain of Baalbek, the famous ruins which travellers to Palestine often go out of their way to see. The Camel had to carry the wood from one village to another. It loitered, turned aside again and again, as a donkey will turn when it sees a wayside thistle; and the boy, getting impatient, struck it several times. The Camel " said nothing " at the time, but stored up the injury in his memory.

A few days later it fell to the lad to lead this Camel back to his own village. No load hampered the creature this time : and his thoughts were busy. He plodded on till they had got about half-way, and were well out of hearing of the village folk. Then the Camel suddenly came to a standstill, and taking a good look round to see that there was no one near, he seized the boy's head in his great mouth, swung him high into the air and dashed him dead upon the ground.

Having taken his revenge, the Camel continued his journey

as if nothing had happened.   But some men had seen the whole incident. They came hurrying up, found the boy lying dead and horribly disfigured, and, hastening after the Camel, they killed the vicious brute on the spot.

The British Empire, with its frequent " little wars," employs a great many Camels. They go with the troops as baggage-carriers.

The pity of it is that too often the poor Camel is put into the charge of native servants who understand little or nothing about him, and how he should be treated. He gets kicked and whacked and dragged hither and thither in a way that would break the heart of any animal. His habits and his few needs are either not known or not respected, and he is made to do things which nature never intended him to do.

For example, a Camel will go far, but he must go at his own pace. To force him to go faster is to kill him. Then, again, although he does not want much food, nor dainty food, he must have it regularly. If not, his nice firm hump gets flabby and soft, and becomes smaller and smaller. And yet again, nature fitted him to live in lands where the climate is dry—whether it be warm or cold. His feet are formed to travel over loose sand, even over rough roads among the hills, but not over wet slippery places at all.

But all these things are forgotten or disregarded when he becomes an army Camel. A leisurely creature, he finds himself in the midst of bustle and excitement. He is hurried about, he is left unfed till he can be attended to, and he is made to traverse all sorts of unsuitable places.

What happens? Well, just what you might expect. The poor Camel comes to grief. And the British soldier looks upon him as a great sulky, slow-going, tiresome brute, who is always in trouble himself and is always getting other people into trouble. The soldier's poet, Mr. Rudyard Kipling, puts all this into some droll verses, in which he makes the Cockney soldier complain of the Camel after this manner :

> "'E'll lose 'isself for ever if you let 'im stray a mile;
> 'E's game to graze the 'ole day long an' 'owl the 'ole night through,
> And when 'e comes to greasy ground 'e splits 'isself in two."

Really, it seems as if the only person who understands the Camel and takes proper care of him is the Arab. Even he is a hard master, but he is not an unreasonable one, and he does not expect his humped servant to do things for which he is not fitted.

It is a shameful thing that when we English use Camels in war—on the Indian frontier and elsewhere—we always *misuse*

A TRAIN OF INDIAN CAMELS READY TO MARCH.

them. In the Afghan War it is reckoned that we used up no less than 20,000 of these useful beasts. They died, for the most part, not of wounds, but of sheer ill-treatment and mismanagement. Think of the waste of money. Think, too, of the suffering that went on among the poor brutes, whom everybody scolded and no one seemed to have time to pity!

In the more recent war in Somaliland (1903) the Camels

seem to have been in much better hands. The Somalis in the British service would be heard singing to their Camels, at daybreak, when they were getting ready to start. The headman would lead off with a line, and the others would repeat it twice. In the dim light the singing sounded pleasantly to sleepy ears :

> "One day and one night more, Camel.
> One day and one night more, Camel.
> One day and one night more, Camel."

And then would come another burst of singing, in which the Camel was supposed to make answer.:

> "Come, load me quickly:
> Come, load me quickly."

The Pack-Camel is the one best known, perhaps, to English readers, but there is a fleet-footed, high-bred species of Camel which is used almost entirely for riding. This is the Dromedary.

Although in Eastern eyes a Dromedary is such a swift beast, it seldom moves at a greater pace than eight or ten miles an hour. But when we know that this can be kept up, without a halt, for twenty hours, we see how wonderful is its staying-power. Thirty-seven strides a minute is often the rule, measuring from six to seven feet in the stride.

To any one not used to ride one of these swift Camels the seat is a most uncomfortable one, the shaking and jerking and jolting being dreadful.

The ordinary riding Camel, however, makes a good enough " mount." Mr. F. L. James, in his *Wild Tribes of the Soudan*, says : " I much prefer a Camel to a horse as a mode of conveyance in Africa. The motion of a good Camel is not tiring when once you get accustomed to it, which you very soon do ; and it will travel at the rate of about five miles an hour for hours together."

This writer seems to have been specially fortunate in his steed. He says : " My animal used to make scarcely any noise when I wanted to mount or dismount — a rare virtue in Camels. A slight jerk at the rope which did duty as a bridle, and he would go off at a trot. He never had a sore back (a very common thing when a Camel's saddle is not properly adjusted to his hump), and his coat was wonderfully clean, instead of being covered with ticks as most Camels are."

I have said that the Arab makes the best master for a Camel. I might add, it is the Arab who gets most out of him. His flesh is a very welcome addition to his master's larder, though only on rare occasions can so precious an animal be killed for

PLOUGHING WITH CAMELS.

food. The milk of a milch-Camel is most often drunk when it has turned sour—such is Arab taste—and part of the day's supply is churned into butter. When a Camel dies, his skin, like that of the American bison in years gone by, is made into a very serviceable cloak ; and the long coarse hair, which a Camel sheds at certain seasons, is spun into thread of a strong, useful kind.

As it was in ancient times, so nowadays, a herd of Camels is a valuable possession : to have many is to be rich.

THE BACTRIAN CAMEL.

When, some few years ago, there was a rush of gold-diggers to Klondyke, in North America, great hardships were suffered in that snowy region owing to the scarcity of food. The nearest town was so very far away, and everything had to be brought to the mining camps on sledges, drawn by men or dogs.

When Herr Hagenbeck, the wild beast collector at Hamburg,

A CAMEL TEAM ON THE STEPPES.

heard of this difficulty he made a suggestion. Of all kinds of carriers, he wrote, "the best animal for the Klondyke climate is the big Siberian Camel. These Camels transport all merchandise from China to Russia, and can stand Siberian cold as well as the greatest heat. They never need shelter, and sleep out in the deep snow. They can carry from five to six hundredweight; they will go in harness, too, and can pull as much as a big horse. They can cross mountains as well as level country." And he offered to buy them in Asia and ship them to New York for sale at a given price—£60 a piece.

Herr Hagenbeck was thinking of the great two-humped Bactrian Camel. Any one who has travelled in Northern Asia knows how widely this hardy animal is used as a carrier. On those vast bleak plains of Central Asia hundreds of thousands of them wander and feed, and the men who conduct the great caravan trade between East and West are seldom without as many of them as they require.

BACTRIAN CAMELS ON THE MONGOLIAN STEPPES.

The Bactrian Camel is rather more stoutly built than the Arabian, and his pace is very slow—say, two and a half miles an hour. But if he is slow he is sure. Those broad, plodding feet of his trudge on hour after hour, in the most unwearying way.

When he is being loaded, if too much is piled on, he will often refuse to rise to his feet until part of the load is taken off. But, once set going, he keeps going, and cases have been known where he has literally died marching, dropping without a warning.

He will carry tea-chests—China tea intended for selling in

13

Russia—up to four or five hundredweight. "So loaded, he will make his way up mountain paths 12,000 feet above sea-level." And year after year the same animals will be found engaged in this work. It is reckoned that something like ten thousand Bactrian Camels pass in or out of the gates of Peking daily, during the winter !

This Camel will even allow himself to be harnessed to a vehicle—the *tarantass*, for example, a springless waggon in which the traveller can lie as in a bed (a very jolting and trying one, it is true).

His food is of the coarsest ; he will crop the driest, dustiest herbage by the wayside ; but he must have water every three days. He will even drink from lakes and pools that are quite briny. As for his hardiness it is positively surprising. Neither sun-glare nor piercing cold seem to do him any harm. The burning sun and the wintry wind and snow assail his thick-coated body in vain.

Long ago, when Russia was ruled by a woman, the Empress Catherine, the Tartars, who had moved westward, declared they would be Russian subjects no longer ; and trekked, as the Boers would say, back to the deserts where their forefathers lived.

There were several hundred thousands who went, and they had many Camels. But a pursuer, fiercer than any Russian lancer, was soon at their heels. They might defy the Empress : they could not defy King Winter. By day the cold was dreadful ; by night it was deadly. Huddling for warmth around the camp-fires, men, women, and children would be found frozen to death when the morning light returned. But of the Camels scarcely any perished in that terrible *trek*.

The Bactrian Camel is very sure-footed. He is quite at home even on ice and snow. Instances have been known where out of a train of two thousand Camels brought over a mountain range only one was lost, and that through an accident.

When Sven Hedin, the famous explorer, was crossing the Pamirs—those desolate uplands that lie to the north-west of India, and have been called the Roof of the World—he found the deep snow very fatiguing to plunge through, until he hit upon the happy idea of making his Camels go before him, treading a path through the drifts with their broad, leather-padded feet.

The Camel is also more or less proof against the terrible dust-storms and sand-storms which are so common, alike on

THE BACTRIAN CAMEL—A GRAND SPECIMEN.

[From a Photograph.

the windy uplands of Central Asia and the burning deserts of Africa. The grit that blinds and chokes human beings powders him in vain. For the Camel has the power of closing his nostrils in such a way as to shut out the dust.

Indeed, one authority, Major Cumberland, believes that the large number of wild Camels in Turkestan, round about Kashgar, are the descendants of herds whose masters perished in a great sand-storm which swept over the district, about two centuries ago.

The Simoom, which is one of the dangers of the African desert, is sighted or scented a long way off by travelling Camels. Down they go in a moment, doubling their legs under them, and stretching out their long necks flat on the ground. They poke their noses into the loose sand ; and their Arab riders, knowing at once what it all means, make haste to throw themselves on their faces with their cloaks over their heads. The air grows thick, the sun is hidden, and the storm sweeps upon them, but, thanks to these weather-wise animals, it finds every one prepared.

THE KANGAROO.

IT is quite possible that some new animal, quite different from any that we know, may even yet be discovered, overrun though the world is, and almost every corner of it well searched by now. But it is not likely that any ship will bring home to England a new creature so utterly unlike anything known before as did the *Endeavour*, Captain Cook's long-voyaged ship, which brought back the skin of the *Kangaroo*.

It was in the year 1770 that this vessel was feeling its way along what we now know to be the coast of Queensland. She had had a close shave of being wrecked on that strange, long chain of rocks, the Great Barrier Reef, and her captain when he came to the mouth of a river running into the sea (since named after the ship) stopped there for repairs.

There was none too much food aboard, and when a party of sailors was told off to go ashore and see if a few animals and birds could be obtained, some of which might prove to be worth cooking, the tars went willingly enough.

Back they came, in due course, and their muskets had not been idle. But the most interesting part of the report they brought back was their story of a new and extraordinary animal. It had a deer-like head, and long, noticeable ears, and a thick, soft-looking, grey, furry coat; but its attitude and its movements were most odd. When at rest it sat back on its hind legs with its strong tail to balance it; and when it was startled into flight it did not run away on all fours, but went off in a series of flying jumps, so long and easy that it would have been idle to attempt to overtake it.

The ship's naturalist, who was no other than Sir Joseph Banks, must have been a happy man that night, though a curious and impatient one; and it was not until a day or two later that his curiosity was satisfied. Then a specimen of the animal—the Great Grey Kangaroo—was shot and brought to the ship.

How interested and surprised the man of science must have been, as he examined the queer creature—most of all when he noticed the strange pouch or pocket in the front of its body, in which its young could be carried about, and hidden away at the approach of danger.

It was found, ere long, that a whole race of animals, in Australia, were pouch-bearers (*Marsupials*, if you prefer the Latin word); but the Kangaroo, because of its size, is about the best example of animals having this very curious feature.

Really there are few sights in the animal world more quaint than that of a mother Kangaroo sitting up, with the sharp-nosed, sharp-eared head of her youngster peeping out of her pouch. Presently the little one jumps out, and begins to nibble a bit at any green leaf that its dainty fancy chooses. But at the least scare it flies back to its cosy hiding-place.

The clan of the Kangaroo is a very big one. First, by virtue of his great size and strength, comes the Great Grey Kangaroo— the " Boomer " or the " Old Man," as he is variously called by Colonials. The Woolly or Red Kangaroo is a good second, being nearly as large. He is found mostly in the south and eastern parts of Australia, on rocky ground; his colour, despite his name, is, for the most part, yellowish rather than reddish.

After these two giants come the smaller-sized Wallabies : the Rock Wallaby, a night-rover, who must be sought for in hilly and rocky districts, and is a most agile " skipper " ; the Black Wallaby, whose flesh makes a most appetising dish, the Brush-tail Wallaby, and others. Then there are the Tree Kangaroos, of no great size and by no means very nimble. They live in New Guinea and in the hottest parts of Queensland, and they have to be sought for in the thick forests and dense scrub. They are said to climb slowly and clumsily, as if " not to the manner born." But, as Dr. Johnson remarked about the dancing dog, the thing is not that he should dance on his hind legs so awkwardly, but that he should dance at all. So, in the case of the Tree Kangaroo, the wonder is that one of these heavy-tailed, ground-hopping animals should have ever been able to get up into a tree-top at all.

KANGAROO HUNTING IN AUSTRALIA.

[*Drawn by* SCOTT RANKIN.

FEMALE.

MALE.

RED KANGAROO.

Altogether there are some twenty different species of the Kangaroo family; but we cannot deal here with the lesser members. Something more, however, should be said about the Great Grey Kangaroo, who is a very fine and striking beast indeed.

A full-grown specimen will measure as much as five feet from the nose to the root of the tail, and the tail adds another four feet or so to his length. In weight he will scale anything from 150 to 200 lbs. He has the soft brown Kangaroo eyes, but he has spirit and strength enough to make him a most formidable foe.

Things cannot have been altogether peaceful for the "Boomer," even before white men came planting and building and shooting in his vast island home. For the blacks were there long before Captain Cook or Dampier or Tasman came sailing to those southern seas. And, in a practised hand, the bone-tipped spear and the strange twisted boomerang, thrown with wonderful skill by those savages, laid low many of his tribe.

Indeed, not content with "stalking" him—creeping upon him unawares, with all the stealth and cunning of his race—the black Aborigine would collect his relatives and friends, and arrange a "drive."

Silently they would surround a troop of Kangaroos feeding in the open, and at a given signal close in upon them from all sides. The startled animals would lose their wits, and fly hither and thither; but meeting the yelling blacks wherever they rushed, and frightened by the spears and other missiles flung at them, they would crowd together, and be all laid low in a very short time.

Sometimes, the better to scare the poor beasts, the dry grass would be set alight, and a long line of leaping flames would drive them towards their armed foes waiting to strike them down.

The savage feast that always followed a drive of this sort was a sight enough to sicken a white visitor—for the feasters gorged themselves till they could not eat another mouthful, devouring the flesh with a greediness that was horrid to watch.

The number of Kangaroos on the plains of Australia, even a century ago, must have been very great; but in many districts they are now quite scarce. For flocks and herds have come to the grass lands, and they have come to stay. In a dry season there is often not enough green food for the newcomers and the old dwellers, and, say the stockmen, the old must go.

So the "Boomer" is hunted down without mercy. And, as the love of sport is as widespread in English Colonies as in England itself, the men who have made their homes in those new lands contrive that the Kangaroo shall provide them with an excuse for some hard, exciting riding.

Horses and dogs turn out for a Kangaroo hunt, and the run that a healthy "Boomer," or "Forester," as he is sometimes called, can give them within a few hours is surprising.

Here is a first-hand description of such a hunt. It occurred in Tasmania. "I recollect one day in particular when a very fine Boomer jumped up in the midst of the hounds in the ' open.' He at first took a few jumps with his head up, in order to look about him, to see on which side the coast was clearest, and, without hesitating a moment, he started forward and shot away from the hounds, apparently without an effort, and gave us the longest run I ever saw after a Kangaroo. He ran fourteen miles by the map, from point to point ; and if he had had fair play I believe he would even then have beaten us. But he had gone along a tongue of land which ran into the sea, so that, being hard pressed, he was forced to try to swim across the arm of sea, which cannot have been less than two miles wide here."

One is sorry to read that after this gallant race for life he was not spared. Wind and sea were against him, and, strong swimmer though he was, he could not long make headway. He turned back, and reaching the beach, "faint and exhausted, he was soon killed." Counting the twists and curves in his course, he must have run eighteen miles, and to be able to swim a mile out to sea and a mile back, after such a race, shows how remarkable is the strength and endurance of the Great Grey Kangaroo.

Kangaroos move by leaps and bounds, and when in full flight can easily cover fifteen or sixteen feet at each spring. The ordinary hedges and fences used on a sheep-run or cattle station are easily overleaped. This makes them most troublesome visitors where there are crops growing, for they find out these cultivated lands and come there to feast.

If a Kangaroo can get away from his enemy, man, he will do so, but when overtaken and cornered he is a dangerous opponent. Only an inexperienced hunter and an untrained dog will ever think of rushing in upon a Boomer at bay. With his back to a tree (if he can find one) the animal awaits his foes. His long, sinewy hind legs can reach far, and they are armed with a great sharp nail or spur which can tear open the body of a dog at a stroke. His short fore-paws also are very strong, and ever ready to seize a too daring assailant.

A hunter tells the following story of how this trick nearly cost him his life. One of his dogs had been killed by a kick from the Boomer's terrible hind foot, and he was so enraged at the loss that he ran in to despatch the creature. He had brought a thick stick, and when he struck with it the weapon shivered into pieces! It had been unused for a long time, and white ants had eaten the heart out.

The next instant he found himself clutched, weaponless and helpless, between the monster's fore-paws, while the great hind-toe tried to treat him as it had treated the dog. He found his strength failing, his other dog had been badly hurt and would not come near, and he could neither kill his captor nor get away from him.

Suddenly, there was a shout, and the hope of rescue gave him strength to tear himself from the sharp claws, and spring for a tree-trunk close by. He had scarcely done this when a bullet struck the trunk close to his head. The next shot hit the Kangaroo, which rolled over dead.

The panting hunter came out from his shelter to find that his deliverers were no other than his brother and a friend. They had at first mistaken him for the Kangaroo.

Often, a Boomer, when sorely driven, will make for the nearest water-hole or pool, and, sitting in it bolt upright, will catch the first dog that rushes or swims towards him, and hold it under water till it drowns.

Kangaroo dogs are strong, swift animals, specially bred for this kind of hunting. They are a cross between a greyhound and a staghound. No ordinary dog would have any chance of overtaking so fleet a quarry.

When a mother Kangaroo is chased she will sometimes turn

aside and take the little one (Australians call them " joeys ") from her pouch, and place it in a bush or a clump of long grass, and then continue her flight. If she escapes the hunters she will come back and fetch the queer little creature. She is a watchful and faithful mother.

Many of these abandoned " joeys " have been found by hunters, and some have been sent home to England. Often they die on the voyage, but some have lived to gladden their owners in this country. At the Duke of Bedford's wonderful open-air " preserve " at Woburn Abbey, at Lord Rothschild's seat at Tring, and at other places, Kangaroos have been given a home that seems to suit them, and in which they appear to be quite happy.

The Kangaroo House at the London Zoo is usually well supplied with these wonderfully active animals, with their sharp claws and their soft brown eyes.

Among the late Frank Buckland's many stories was one which proves that if Kangaroos are enemies that can fight fiercely, they are also friends that can love fondly.

He says that a pair of them, named Flora and Jack, had been sent from Australia to Philadelphia, in the United States. Arrived at Liverpool, for some reason Flora was sent on in advance. She was miserable, and could think of nothing but her absent mate. Her cries were piteous.

However, it was not long before a fresh party of four-footed travellers were brought to the menagerie. Among them was Jack. Flora seemed to know at once, and called to him. When he answered she was wild with joy, and so boisterous did the two become that the keeper at last opened the door of Flora's cage, and allowed these loving friends to greet one another again.

Nothing could be more joyful and fond than that greeting. It was quite touching to see them caressing one another in their delight at being together once more.

THE BABOON.

WE know a great deal more about the Baboon than was known half a century and less ago, but for a long time before that stories were brought home by African travellers which told of the strength, the courage, and the cunning of the dog-faced ape—the ugliest animal, perhaps, in all the world.

He seems scarcely to deserve being classed among the mirthful and amusing monkey tribe. He is like a grim burglar among a lot of light-hearted schoolboys. Captured and tamed, indeed, he is said to become often very attached to his owner if kindly treated, but in his natural wild state he is a fierce, cunning, formidable fellow, whom even the larger beasts of prey respect, and often hesitate to attack.

Necessity seems to have made the Baboon a fighter. He is not a tree-dweller, able to seek safety among the high branches at a moment's notice, like the monkeys we call to mind. He lives in the open, on rocky hillsides, if he can get such, but frequently he descends into the plains, and there, of course, he is still more easily attacked.

So, as with a good many human beings, danger sharpened his wits. He came to understand that the only safe way of moving about in the midst of his enemies was by keeping near his fellows. Singly he had no chance—the swift rush of a lion, the cat-like pounce of a leopard, found him practically helpless if alone, though before he died he might, indeed, inflict on his foe a grievous wound with his long, tusk-like teeth.

Therefore Baboons go about in troops. They have learned to act together not only against a common enemy, but even in such things as the getting of food. When there is not enough to be had close to their headquarters, they make an expedition to rob the cultivated ground belonging to some neighbouring farm.

The raid is as carefully planned as the Border raids and forays that used to take place between the Scots and the English in the olden days—the days of Chevy Chase. Scouts are sent on in advance to see whether the coast is clear, the females and the young ones are kept in the centre of the little army, and the veterans push to the front.

Should the alarm be given while the corn or the pumpkins are being stolen, the veterans "cover the retreat," chattering and showing their great teeth, and all the time retiring, till the whole party is out of reach of its pursuers.

These expeditions are a very real trouble to the farmer. For there are often as many as two and three hundred Baboons taking part in them, and these can gather a very large quantity of fruit and grain between them.

One modern traveller declares that he is sure that Baboons have a language of their own, and that in danger the old animals in the troop give their directions by means of certain cries with distinct meanings—"words of command" like those given to our soldiers. And he tells us that it is most amusing during a retreat, or hasty removal, to watch how the veterans cuff and drub the unruly youngsters who are slow in obeying orders or dare to stray "out of the ranks."

The same authority says : "It is most interesting to watch the troops of Baboons as they go to drink, of an afternoon between four and five o'clock, and to note how cautiously they quench their thirst."

Their great object is to avoid the crocodiles. Baboons never drink without having the water watched and guarded by some old and experienced members of their troop, either from a tree or from the shore.

"The moment a crocodile is sighted, the alarm is given. Like lightning the whole troop tear up into the trees for safety, and give vent to their anger in a chorus of grunts and squeaks. From their high watch-towers the sentinel Baboons keep an eye on any movement of the crocodile, and it is only after the most cautious survey that the troop are allowed once more to draw near

THE BABOON.

the water to drink, or make for some shallower spot, where the crocodile could not so easily get at them."

Baboons have marvellous powers of espying things at a distance ; and this, joined to a very keen sense of smell, makes them most useful "watch-dogs" when they have been tamed and trained. They themselves can slip past sentinels, whether animal or human, in the most noiseless and clever manner, but the lightest footfall when *they* are on duty is at once detected and the alarm raised.

Baboons are also said to have the power of discovering places where water is likely to be found, when, as so often happens in the regions where they live, the supply in the wells and pools has run short.

They can be trained to do many things, but their temper is so uncertain that many owners of Baboons prefer not to run the risks which such training involves. (The keeper of the Chacma Baboon at the London Zoo once declared that he " would rather go into the lion's cage than intrude on the Chacma when in a rage ! ")

A crippled signalman on the railway from Port Elizabeth, at a place called Uitenhage, might have been seen, until some few years ago, doing his work with the help of a Baboon. He had trained the creature to draw him along on a trolly to a signal some way off, and there work the lever, while he himself watched to see that it was properly done.

Hideous though he is, there is something so human in a Baboon's ways and intelligence that most sportsmen shrink from shooting one. They say the look in the eyes of a wounded Baboon is as piteous as that of a badly wounded soldier pleading for succour on the battlefield.

His care for the creatures of his own kind is also very human. He will quarrel and fight with his kith and kin, but let one of them be seen to be in danger from an outsider, and at once the whole tribe is up in arms. The German naturalist, Brehm, has a very striking story in his book *From North Pole to Equator*, which well illustrates this.

He was crossing an open space with his dogs—big, strong, Arab greyhounds, which had bowled over many a fierce beast

14

in those regions. Suddenly they came in sight of a troop of Baboons moving over the level ground towards some high rocks, and the dogs flew towards them.

But this time the hounds had a surprise. The Baboons got ready for defence in their usual way, the males facing the foe with their long white teeth gleaming and their eyes flashing dangerously, while the females and the young ones slipped past to the rocks and safety. The dogs shrank back, as well they might, and the rearguard of the Baboon army retired growling to the rocks.

One little six-months-old Baboon, however, had been overlooked and left behind, and the dogs closed round it. But the sharp eyes of its relatives had seen it, and suddenly an old veteran let himself down from the rock ledge and all alone crept out to the rescue. His great fierce face and powerful arms and hands awed the dogs, and before they could summon up pluck to spring at him, he had seized the little creature and climbed back to his comrades. It was just the sort of act that among human beings would have merited the Victoria Cross.

The same naturalist had, like many other travellers, another and less pleasant proof of the formidableness of the Baboon. He and his companion had ventured into a pass, where the rocks were alive with the bobbing heads of these warlike animals, and the two men were forced in a very short time to run for their lives. For the Baboons flung stones at them from the heights, and even rolled down boulders upon their supposed foes, two or more uniting to set these moving !

These cliff-haunting and stone-throwing habits of the Baboon were noticed and recorded by the first voyagers who made his acquaintance. The story has been preserved for us, though the voyage took place five hundred and twenty years before the Christian era. Curiously enough, the name " Gorilla," which nowadays stands for a much larger and more terrible ape, was given to the creatures seen by those old-world explorers.

It was from Carthage, then one of the greatest cities in the world, but now utterly destroyed, that the expedition was sent out. Hanno, who commanded it, seems to have sailed down the west coast of Africa, as far as Sierra Leone, and, in a bay known then as the Horn of the South, he says there was an island " full of wild men, with hairy bodies, whom the interpreters called *Gorillas*. But, pursuing them, we were not able to take the males ; they all escaped, being able to climb the precipices, and defended themselves with pieces of rock. But three females, who bit and scratched those who led them, were not willing to follow. However, having killed them, we flayed them, and conveyed the skins to Carthage.''

The rocks and cliffs are the Baboon's real home, and among such they are found from Egypt to Cape Town, where numbers of them still prowl about Table Mountain, and occasionally do a great deal of mischief. They are found also in Guinea and other parts of West Africa.

There are several species of Baboons, each with a distinct name—the Chacma, the Mandrill, the Papion, etc.

The Mandrill is one of the strangest and most repulsive-looking of animals, with its grotesque colour-streaked face. And as for the Chacma, with its enormously strong arms and shoulders, and savage, tusk-like teeth, he is a sight to test anybody's courage, as he comes creeping nimbly on all fours to do battle with the man or beast who has angered him.

Let me close with a present-day story. In May 1906 the *Comrie Castle* arrived at Plymouth from Cape Town. The liner had on board a number of wild animals, which were being brought to England for sale. Among these were several Baboons. When the ship had been seven days at sea, one of the Baboons broke loose from its cage in the hold, and nearly got up on to the deck among the passengers. It was prevented, but to secure it was quite another matter. Nets were used for the purpose, but the Baboon, agile like most of its kind, easily avoided being entangled by springing to a great height.

Then the keeper and Herr Windhorn, the proprietor, pluckily made their way into the hold and faced the great brute. (He was four and a half feet high.) Unluckily, Herr Windhorn tripped over the matting and fell. In an instant the Baboon was upon him, and fastened its teeth in his leg.

Seizing the creature's head, he tried to wrench open the jaws which had closed on him like a vice, but the beast only let go to snap at his hand, hurting it badly. The keeper and the boat-swain came to his help, getting bitten themselves, and the three men managed to make their escape.

For three days the Baboon was at large (for to shoot it would have meant a considerable loss to its purchaser), but at last it was lassoed and hauled back to its cage. Four days later the sullen brute was found dead. The owner gave it as his deliberate opinion that the Baboon " died of a broken heart at being mastered."

From all we know of a Baboon's nature it is quite likely that this explanation was the true one.

THE GORILLA.

IT had long been known that a huge and very savage, ape-like beast existed in the dense, dark forests of Western Africa.

As far back as the days of our Queen Elizabeth, an English seaman, Andrew Battell, who had been captured by the Portuguese, and lived eighteen years in Angola, saw and described the creature.

After that nobody seems to have troubled any further about it for nearly two centuries and a half, when a certain Dr. Savage, an American, obtained several skulls. A little later, the famous African traveller, Paul du Chaillu, gave us the story of his coming face to face with the horrible monster in its forest home.

A finely stuffed specimen of a huge Gorilla and a young one, also stuffed, figured in the Great Exhibition at Paris, in 1855, and aroused great interest. And it was not long before the British Museum was provided with a specimen.

In our days when all rare animals are so mercilessly pursued and caught or killed, it seems strange that the Gorilla should have remained unknown so long (though, to be sure, it is only a few years ago that the Okapi was discovered!).

The chief reasons are that its haunts are at some distance from the coast, and there is little to tempt Europeans to plunge into those moist, unwholesome forests; and that the natives have a very great fear of this enormously strong brute, and do not go out of their way to attack it.

In the account of the Gorilla, written by Battell, the Elizabethan sailor, a good deal of truth was mixed with what was mere hearsay, but his description is worth quoting. Says Battell:

" He is in all proportion like a man, but that he is more like a giant in stature. . . . He goeth always upon his legs. . . . They sleep on the trees and build shelter from the rain. . . . They cannot speak, and have no more understanding than a beast. The people of the country, when they travel in the woods, make fires where they sleep at night, and in the morning, when they are gone, the Pongoes (Gorillas) will come and sit about the fire till it goes out ; for they have no understanding to lay the wood together. . . . These Pongoes are never taken alive, because they are so strong that ten men cannot hold one of them ; but they take many of their young ones with poisoned arrows."

Battell also tells a queer story which many of the natives even nowadays seem to believe, namely, that when elephants come trespassing on their feeding-grounds the Gorillas rush at them, " and so beat them with their clubbed fists and pieces of wood that they run roaring away."

When Du Chaillu's book came out, a great many people would not accept what he told therein about his search for this terrible but little known man-ape, and his encounter with it. Most of my readers will like to have the traveller's story for the most part in his own words :

" Suddenly, as we were creeping along in perfect silence, the woods were filled with the tremendous barking roar of the Gorilla. Then the underbrush swayed rapidly just ahead, and presently before us stood an immense male Gorilla. He had gone through the jungle on all-fours ; but, when he saw our party, he raised himself erect, and looked us boldly in the face.

" He stood about a dozen yards from us, and was a sight I shall never forget. Nearly six feet (he proved to be less by four inches), with immense body, huge chest, and great muscular arms, with fiercely glaring, large, deep-grey eyes, and a fiendish look on his face, which seemed to me like a nightmare : thus stood before us the king of the African forest.

" He was not afraid of us. He stood there, and beat his breast with his huge fists till it resounded like an immense drum, meantime giving roar after roar."

Du Chaillu and his party let him come to within some six yards of them, and then they fired. With a deep groan the giant toppled forward and fell. In a few moments he was dead, and the hunters were able to examine their " kill."

When we say of a Gorilla, as Andrew Battell said of him long ago, that he is *a giant*, bodily strength rather than height is meant.

Specimens measuring six feet high have, indeed, been killed, but the chief thing about a Gorilla is its muscular power and bigness. The breadth of its. chest would make that of a blacksmith seem puny ; its arms are enormously thick and strong, and reach to below the knees, and the hands could tear a man to pieces.

THE GORILLA.

The great head is set deep in the shoulders, and the bite of its huge, gaping mouth is frightful. The fierce eyes are very sunken, and overhung by a bony ridge that gives. the face much of its ferocious lowering look, and Du Chaillu says that when it is enraged the crest of short hair on its sloping forehead twitches up and down.

The Gorilla is stronger than the strongest of men, but what we admire in a strong man—grace and a well-proportioned figure —are not to be found in this, the largest of the apes. He is clumsy and misshapen. Look, for example, at the length of the massive arms. One specimen, which was under five feet and a half in height, measured over eight feet from finger-tips to finger-tips when its arms were stretched out.

The skin of a Gorilla is black, and the hair, which is black or iron-grey, often turns grey or even white with advancing age. The male Gorilla is usually a foot taller than its mate.

Even very young ones, mere babies of two and three years, are most difficult to capture. They bite, and tear, and struggle like little furies, until only the boldest natives will tackle them. And if they are at last made fast and put in a crate or cage, they fly even at the hand that brings them their food, and usually end their imprisonment by dying of sheer rage and resentment.

A Gorilla's proper food consists of fruit and nuts, and to obtain them he tears down branches and often young trees whole-sale. He is a huge eater, and when his favourite berries and nuts are out of season, he and his kind appear to " go on their travels," and may be found " far from home." Du Chaillu speaks of having seen at least two of these wandering troops of Gorillas, each consisting of some eight or ten, mostly females. They will often visit the little patches of cultivated land belonging to the natives, and help themselves to the fruit or vegetables.

The forest trees are the Gorilla's home, and two things which the natives have long averred about his home habits seem to be true.

One is that he builds in the lower branches a sort of rough shelter of twigs and boughs. (There can be little comfort in it, since, as the natives point out, there is no rain-proof cover to it in that land of tropical downpours.) And the other story is that when this shelter becomes a nursery, and mother and young one have to be safeguarded from the attacks of wild beasts, the male Gorilla sleeps below with his back against the tree-trunk, ready to wake and strike out with his heavy paw the moment a leopard or some other intruder comes too near.

A Gorilla walks with his long arms hanging before him, and the fingers touching the ground : and he half swings, half jerks his great body along. He can run very fast. That he stands erect when about to do battle is doubted by some who have seen him in his native solitudes.

The Gorilla's country is a not very broad slice of West Africa ; roughly speaking, it may be said to lie between the Cameroon and Congo rivers. "He lives," says Du Chaillu, "in the loneliest and darkest parts of the dense jungles, preferring deep wooded valleys and also rugged heights. The high plains, strewn with immense boulders, seem also to be favourite haunts. I have noticed that the Gorilla is always found very near to a plentiful supply of water."

He tells us that, although the Gorilla does not attack men unless provoked or cornered, the natives have such respect for the creature's fearful teeth and mighty hands, that they would not think of hunting it except with firearms. And in those parts where the " fire-darting tubes " are unknown (or were unknown, in his day), "this great beast roamed unmolested, the monarch of the forest."

THE BISON.

OF all wild cattle the Bison is the best known, and when we speak of the Bison we are usually thinking of the American Bison.

He, oddly enough, is popularly known as the "Buffalo." It came about in this wise : in new countries the people have rather a careless way of naming the animals and birds which they find there, and so the American settlers and frontiersmen coming upon these great, shaggy-headed cattle on the Western plains took them to be Buffaloes—and called them so—and the name has clung.

But the Bison is not the Buffalo, nor the Buffalo the Bison, and it is a pity that the misleading title was used so long.

However, something far worse than the misnaming of these animals has happened, and that is their extermination, their pitiless and deliberate slaughtering out. So complete has this been that to include

THE AMERICAN BISON

in a book of living animals seems almost like including Queen Anne among "Celebrities I have known." Happily, a few specimens still survive, in the great Yellowstone Park and other preserves in the United States, and also on the Canadian border.

To the boys and girls who may read these pages this will not seem very wonderful, although "a very great pity they are all gone." But to their elders it is almost past belief that the great roving beasts which wandered over those vast plains *in millions*, when *they* were boys and girls, should have all been killed off. "Is it possible ?" they exclaim.

It is indeed a pitiful, and, in some ways, a very shameful story. If we ask who was to blame, the answer is—partly white men, partly the Redskins. And if we search for the cause it is to be traced to the greed of gain. These men learned that good prices were to be had for " buffalo robes," *i.e.* the hides of these animals, and they set to work to " supply the market."

At first the killing had little effect on the immense numbers. Half a dozen hides was in itself a heavy weight, and the pack-horses that brought in the loads had to travel great distances. But at last the great plains began to be crossed by railways, and then for every half-dozen " robes " brought to market a thousand could be carried and whisked away for hundreds of miles to the places where they would be most in demand.

A buffalo robe, properly " dressed," was looked upon as an almost indispensable part of a traveller's outfit—especially if he was going to sleep in the open, and " rough it " generally. No rug was warmer ; wrapped in its folds, hunter or emigrant could sleep without fear under the open sky. From the chill of night and the heavy dews, and even falling rain, the robe gave perfect protection.

The white man was not the first to discover how valuable it was. The Redskin had found that out long before him. He, indeed, had learned how useful was not only the skin, but almost every other part of the great beast. The Bison was well-nigh as necessary to the prairie Indian as the reindeer was and is to the Laplander.

The curtain walls of his wigwam were of Bison skin. Part of his picturesque costume, especially his moccasins, was of the same. At night he laid himself down on a bed of skins; and when he went out to fight he carried on his bare arm a shield of Bison hide, cleverly shrunk and thickened till it was tough enough to ward off the flying arrows of his foes.

The flesh of the animal was his chief food. Most parts were eatable, but the hump was reckoned the greatest dainty, and many a time, in the wasteful spirit of those days, the splendid creature was shot down for the sake of this coveted portion. The tongue, too, was a part almost always sought for. The present writer can remember seeing it on the table at a Christmas dinner when he was a very little boy.

In the books of Ballantyne, Mayne Reid, and other writers

THE AMERICAN BISON (Front View).

of "Far West" stories, the word "pemmican" often occurs, and many a young reader on coming across the word for the first time must have wondered what it meant.

Pemmican was simply shreds of dried Bison flesh. It was very uninviting to look at, and not very palatable to any but those who ate it with " hunger, the best sauce." But like *biltong*, the dried flesh of the antelope, which the Boers of South Africa,

THE AMERICAN BISON (Rear View).

for generations, have ridden on, and fought on, and thriven on, it can keep a man going for hours and days. It saves him all the heavy equipment of provisions and cooking apparatus which so hindered and hampered our troopers when they were trying to corner their active light-riding opponents during the great war.

One Bison cow with a well-developed hump was reckoned to furnish close upon ninety pounds weight of pemmican. The fatter members of the herd supplied the tallow makers with a good part of their stock-in-trade ; as much as a hundred and fifty pounds weight of tallow has been got from one animal.

As for the horns, they made good powder-flasks for the hunter, in those days, and of course many were carried away as hunting trophies. But millions lay for years strewing the prairie, long after the coyotes and carrion birds had picked the last morsel of meat from their fallen bodies, and the skeleton had crumbled away in the long grass.

The vast prairies, unchanged, still stretch from skyline to skyline, but the great crowds of Bisons that browsed over them—

"Herds upon an endless plain,"

to apply Tennyson's phrase—are gone completely and for ever.

Their chief feeding-grounds were the wide grassy lands lying between the Rio Grande and the Saskatchewan. Here even for such great numbers there was ample room, and plenty of food except towards the end of winter. When the snow lay white over their grazing lands, the broad strong noses of the older Bisons would nuzzle and burrow down to the grass even when the layer of snow was deep. So cleverly did they lay bare their food supply that, it is said, the calves of the tame farm-cattle used often to be seen poking their way in to take advantage of the clearing, the good-natured giants letting them feed beside them.

Lewis and Clarke, who have left us many descriptions of what they saw when crossing those vast prairies, were astonished, as well they might be, by the numbers of these animals : " Such was their multitude as they crossed the river that although it was a mile in breadth, the herd stretched, as thickly as they could swim, completely from the one side to the other." And, another time when they watched them, they reckoned that there must be not less than twenty thousand in that army of horns and hoofs.

As a rule the Bison, despite his formidable look, was a peaceful, inoffensive animal, loving nothing better than to move lazily over the vast prairie, browsing where he chose, or to wallow, like the true buffalo, in the nearest pool or swamp, and plaster his black hide with cooling mud, to keep off the insect pests.

But when wounded and not disabled, or when his young ones were in danger, his small, black eyes would blaze with fury, and he would come charging down on his enemy in the most determined way. Woe betide the unlucky hunter who failed to bring him down with a second bullet. He was likely to be dashed to the ground and savagely gored.

Here is an account of such a charge by one who experienced it—J. K. Lord, the famous hunter and trapper. He was good friends with a certain tribe of American Indians, and used to go out with them when they hunted.

On this occasion they had crept as near as they could to the herd without being seen, but before long were sighted—or scented.

" The trumpet-like notes of the older bulls tell us that we are discovered. Concealment is now of no further use—the beasts are crowding together like sheep when scared by a dog. The Indians give a piercing whoop, and we dash wildly after the retreating herd, their tails upheaved, and their horns rattling noisily against one another. The very plain seems to shake—clouds of blinding dust, raised by thousands of hoofs, nearly hide the hunters from each other—whilst a rumbling noise like subdued thunder seems to swallow up all other sounds.

" I soon overtake the rearmost animals, and singling out a young cow, drop her in her tracks ; re-charge my gun, and single out this time a fine old bull. He seems to roll rather than gallop along, his nose nearly touching the grass, and his shaggy brown mane tossing wildly in the breeze."

Neck and neck the horse and the Bison pounded along. Then the hunter got his chance, and fired. The shot did not miss, but the shaggy old veteran turned sharply on hunter and horse. Two other Bisons blocked the way of escape, and the wounded bull " striking the horse on the point of the shoulder sent us both rolling on the plain."

It was a perilous moment, but the Bison kept his eye on the steed, which scrambled to its feet and limped away. The bull did not follow : his injuries were beginning to tell upon him, but he tried hard to keep on his feet, and planted his massive legs wide apart, breathing heavily.

Even the hunter cannot write of his end without pity : " Hurt and frightened as I was, I felt sorry for him. The eyes lost all their fire, and a sad look came into them. His great chest was heaving convulsively ; and low, plaintive sounds, more like sobs than anything else I know of, told in language plain as printed words how terrible were his sufferings. The head dropped, until the nose was nearly touching the ground ; the ponderous body rocked from side to side ; then suddenly the muscles seemed to lose all further power, and with a heavy crash the king of the plain fell dead amidst the grass and wild flowers."

How many Bisons died in that same sad way, we can only guess. Once it was by the arrows of the Red-man ; then came the white hunter with powder and shot, and the herds grew thinner and fewer every year till the year 1883, when the last of them disappeared from the plains of the Great North-West. Truly, it is a most pitiful story.

In the old days, before any one dreamed that the Bison could be " killed out," many devices were used to overtake and capture the shy beast.

Sir John Franklin, who afterwards perished among the Arctic snows, describes one method which he calls " A Buffalo Pound." It was on the same principle as the keddah, still used in India for the capture of elephants.

In this case an enclosure, about a hundred yards across, was strongly fenced in, and roads leading up to it were marked out with stout stakes planted about twenty yards apart. At the entrances to the pound, if it was winter-time, the snow was banked up strong and high, so that when it came to entering the enclosure none of the Bisons would " shy " at the opening and slip out right and left, and get away.

When all was ready the mounted Indians rode away to the back of the herds grazing on the plain, and " shepherded " them towards one or other of the roads to the pound. The great beasts would move off uneasily, knowing nothing of the death-trap awaiting them. Then the Indians raised a clamour that instantly

THE AMERICAN BISON.

[*Drawn by* GEORGE RANKIN.

15

quickened their steps. As the whoops and yells grew louder and louder, the race became a mad rush, in which there was no turning back. Between the lines of posts, easily mistaken for men, the panic-stricken herd rushed by, and into the pound.

As they poured in, arrows and bullets whizzed out from Indian marksmen hidden near the posts behind a screen of leafy boughs. Before long the pound was strewn with dead and dying Bisons, and a great store of meat awaited the successful hunters.

Another trick was the simple one of closing in upon a herd, in four lines, like the four sides of a square, and driving the frightened beasts in upon one another. Too confused to charge boldly through the thin line of their enemies, the animals were shot down with the greatest ease. Fire was sometimes used to still further confuse them, the dry, prairie grass being set alight.

Yet another method, practised alike by the whites and the Redskins, was to get a big herd between them and the edge of a precipice; then, with loud shouts and wild brandishing of rifles, to drive the frightened creatures over the brink. It meant horrible injuries for the Bisons, but a plentiful supply of meat and hides for the hunters.

The Indians knew how to make a " Buffalo " stampede serve their own purpose. Here is an instance of an attempt made in the summer of 1866, against a body of United States infantry.

These soldiers, to the number of eight hundred, many of them veterans of the great American Civil War, were on their way to New Mexico. They had halted on the open prairie, when a strange low roar like distant thunder reached the ears of the men. Suddenly the sound of a galloping horse was heard, and the next moment a scout rode in with the startling news that a great herd of " Buffalo " was sweeping across the plain and heading straight for the camp.

The thunder-roll was now explained—it was the *thud thud* of thousands of hoofs! But how to escape the charge of that immense crowd of shaggy heads was the question. There was no time to form a barricade behind which the troops could shelter, and, indeed, what barrier could resist the shock of such a charge?

On came the maddened Bisons, nearer and ever nearer, and

soon the soldiers could plainly see the cause of the stampede—a band of five hundred mounted Indians driving the herd before them, in the savage hope that it would overrun the camp and trample the occupants to death.

But while the foremost animals were still some way off, the little group of waggons and tents that rose before them, as a rock may stand up in the bed of a river, seemed to daunt them, and dividing into two streams the living torrent rushed by on either side of the camp, injuring no one. The ruse had failed. The camp was saved, and the Indians, grinding their teeth with vexation, turned and rode away.

How terrible would have been the disaster had the trick succeeded can be guessed when we remember that the weight of a full-sized American Bison was often close upon 2000 lbs.

In *The Old Santa Fé Trail* there is a story of two hunters who suddenly sighted a herd of " Buffalo " feeding on the plains. Their steeds—a horse and a mule—were too tired and slow for them to attempt a chase, so, dismounting, the two men worked their way stealthily towards the herd. As they crept up, themselves being hidden, they saw the sentinels of the herd suddenly take alarm. They turned, the whole herd turned : they stared across at the horse and mule tethered in the distance, and— " went for them."

In a cloud of dust the herd rushed by, and when the two hunters hurried back to the place where they had left their mounts, the poor beasts were nowhere to be seen. They had been carried forward by that great black mob, and trampled out of existence. Of horse and mule, saddle and reins, there was not a vestige left !

Not only in attack, but also in defence, the American Bison was formidable. He had good reason to fear the wolf pack, and his plan was very much the same as that of soldiers who " form square " when they have to " receive cavalry " ; only instead of flashing bayonets there was a line of sharp horns.

As soon as the herd scented a pack of wolves drawing near, they quickly ranged themselves in a ring, the strong ones on the outside, the weak and ailing ones in the centre. Thus they would defy the attacks of their ravenous foes, whose only chance was to wait their time and fall upon some fat or sick member of the herd, or some venturesome calf, when its strong protectors were not near.

Before we pass from this wonderfully interesting subject of the American Bison, I may mention that the Americans themselves are now most anxious that this noble beast should not die out. They have formed an association to protect it—the American Bison Society—which keeps a jealous watch on the small herds still existing, such as the Corbin Herd, in the Blue Mountain Forest Game Preserve.

But the American Bison is not the only one. Our ancestors, until Queen Elizabeth's day, or even later, knew nothing of the great herds that were then roaming in millions over the untraversed prairies of the Far West. But they knew very well, especially a thousand years ago and more,

THE EUROPEAN BISON.

They found him one of the most powerful, most fearless, most dogged of all their four-footed foes, and they respected him greatly. The Aurochs, as he was called, was indeed a shy, retiring sort of beast, who would rather avoid man than fight him, but when roused he could be a terrible opponent, and his immense strength made his capture no easy task.

The wild dense forests of Central Europe, especially those parts where the great rivers made miles of reedy swamps, gave cover to any number of this surly Bison. To-day he is gone. Roads have been cut through the forests, daylight has been let in on the old gloomy retreats where he loved to hide, and the swamps have to a large extent been drained. It is true that in the Forest of Bielowitza, in Lithuania, the Czar of Russia owns a herd which is allowed to roam wild, but it is all the time jealously protected from outside interference.

This herd is counted from time to time; at the close of the Crimean War there were nearly two thousand of these animals in the Forest; in 1882 the numbers had dropped to six hundred;

in 1889 there were less than four hundred ; but in 1892 they had increased to nearly five hundred.

This Bison is a splendid creature, standing close upon six feet high at the shoulder, and with a length sometimes of ten feet from the muzzle to the root of the tail ; while its weight has been known to reach seventeen hundred pounds. Its thick, curly mane is of a rich brown. It feeds on grass and herbage, and the bark of young trees ; and it takes six years to grow to its full size.

Two specimens, young ones, of this Lithuanian breed were presented to our London Zoo by the Czar about the middle of last century.

Fifty hunters and three hundred trackers were employed to capture them. They surrounded the remote valley in which the Bisons were found to be feeding : and at a given signal a horn was sounded.

At once the herd leapt to its feet and stood on the alert, and then began to move off. But they were suddenly brought up short by the line of trackers, who received them with shouts and yells and firing of guns.

The great beasts now thoroughly startled charged furiously. The trackers let them pass ; it was the young ones they had orders to take. Two of these were singled out and captured, one of them being only three months old. The other, a bull of fifteen months, resisted fiercely; eight men threw themselves upon it, and tried to bind it, but it tossed and thrust them all aside, flinging several of them to the ground. Only after much trouble was it secured.

The two little creatures were brought to England, and a cow was chosen to be their foster-mother. Notwithstanding the dislike which was thought to separate Bison from tame cattle, the calves became very fond of their new parent ; but, in spite of the care taken of them, they died a few months after their arrival.

It is to be hoped that this Lithuanian herd will long be protected, and that its numbers will increase. There is, however, one other place where the Bison is found wild, and that is in the mountain solitudes of the Caucasus. Here a few favoured sportsmen, grand-dukes and the like, occasionally are allowed to shoot a specimen, but only by express permission of the Czar.

HUNTING THE BISON IN EUROPE TWO THOUSAND YEARS AGO.

[*Drawn by* COLBRON PEARSE.

COMMON SEALS.

CRAB-EATING SEAL.

THE SEALS.

THERE has always been something specially interesting and mysterious about Seals. Our forefathers certainly thought so. Their stories about Seals are mixed with all manner of quaint fancies. In out-of-the-way places these legends are still repeated, and others that have died out as folk-tales may still be met with in books.

It is only during the last fifty years or thereabouts that the habits of the Seal have come to be really well known. In the olden time it was hard to learn much about an animal which slid so easily and so stealthily from beach to deep sea, and from deep sea to beach. It came up out of the water—out of those dim sea-depths, where all manner of marvellous and terrible things might be lurking. Where other animals would soon have grown tired, and after a little floundering would have sunk and been drowned, this strange creature seemed as much at home as on land. It was like a fish in the water, with a fish-like tail and fish-like fins, or rather flippers, but it was clearly not a fish.

Yet the clumsy way in which it moved about when on shore showed that it really belonged to the sea. It lived on fish, and when scared it made for the water, dived in and disappeared.

But if it was a sea-monster, it was not one of the terrifying kind which assailed the poor mariner. Seafarers, indeed, reported having often met with it when they were far from land, and they had found it quite harmless.

Some of them told how when one of their number had chanced to be playing on some instrument, a Seal's head rose out of the water, and then another, and still another, till a little army of them came swimming after the ship, lured by the music.

The eyes of a Seal are often very soft and beautiful, and full of expression. Hence the stories of mermaids rising up around

233

a ship to steal the heart of the lonely sailor, longing for a glimpse of the faces left far away on shore.

Hence, too, the weird stories that we may still hear in Western Ireland, and, especially, in the wilder parts of Scotland, about Seals coming ashore ; and how some bold watcher would sprinkle one of them with " holy water," got from the priest ; and how that one Seal would cast off her sealskin disguise, and show herself in her true form, as a beautiful maiden, ready to marry the man who had saved her from the power of the enchantment.

And with these would be other and sadder stories telling how the Seal-wife, after several years of happy home-life, would hear " the call of the sea," and slip into the cast-off skin, and be away to the beach where the grey waters were lap-lapping in the moonlight. And there, with one long sigh of regret, and one backward look towards the cosy home she had quitted, she would plunge into the sea, never to return.

In the old days when Seals came landwards at a part of the coast where they were not known, they caused quite a commotion.

It is said that in the reign of our Henry II. a Seal was taken in the river, not far from Orford Castle, in the county of Suffolk.

No one in the neighbourhood seems to have known what the creature was. The men of the castle garrison insisted that it must be a human being, perhaps under the power of an evil spirit, or changed and made dumb by witchcraft. So they treated it as they would have treated an obstinate prisoner. But neither pain nor coaxing drew from it any plain words.

They then took their captive into the church, thinking, as people used to think, in those days, that, at the sight of the big crucifix, the creature (or the dumb spirit dwelling in it) would cry out, and show great signs of awe and terror. But the poor animal only stared around and fidgeted about uneasily,—was ever a Seal taken to church in the world before ?

So the men-at-arms, much perplexed, carried their sleek prisoner back to the castle, and made arrangements for its being kept there, no doubt in the castle courtyard. They gave it fish to eat, and allowed it to go for a swim in the river. For a time it seemed content with its new home, but one day it swam away, and got back to the sea.

THE SEA-LION, AT THE ZOOLOGICAL GARDENS.

We know a good deal more about Seals than did the people of those old days. In the centuries that have passed since Henry the Second's reign, English sailors and those of other nations have voyaged north and south, and seen the Seal families at home, where they could be reckoned by thousands along the lonely beaches and on the ice-fields of the Polar Seas.

The mariners brought back reports of strange dwarfish people, clad in furs from head to foot, who hunted the Seal with sharp lances, who would have been sadly at a loss without this animal, and who used up every particle of it when they caught one.

Seal-fat meant to them oil for softening their hard fare and for lighting their dingy little *igloos* (huts); the flesh was their favourite food. Seal-skins stretched over a framework of whale-bone gave them boats to go hunting in, and tents for living in, through the short, warm, Arctic summer. Out of the sinews a sort of strong thread could be got, the needle being a splinter of bone properly pierced at one end and sharpened at the other. Even the blood was saved, and used for cooking operations.

Much of this the early explorers saw and took note of. But the day came when ships went north and south specially to capture these useful animals, and bring cargoes of their skins back to Europe. Then those people who went after them were less inclined to study the habits of the Seal and the Eskimo's use of his dead body, than to seek out the places where he could be got at most easily and killed in the largest numbers.

Ever since then the killing of Seals has been steadily going on. Hundreds of thousands have sometimes been slaughtered in a single season. Sealskin jackets have been one of the fashions in Europe and America for many years. And the ships' crews sail away year by year to " supply the demand."

A sad story and a very horrible one could be told of the way the sealers, armed with bludgeons and skinning knives, land where the Seals are lying on the ice, harmless and unsuspicious, and go up and down, hither and thither, knocking them on the head, till the ice is strewn with their dead bodies, and made red with their blood. It is an ugly business, very.

The part of the year when the baby Seals are born is spent at certain favourite haunts. The Seals come swimming from far

away in shoals, all making for the rocks they know so well.   Away
up in the cold seas that flow between the nearly touching corners
of Asia and America—Behring Straits is the name—are the
Pribyloff Islands ; these draw the greatest crowds, perhaps,
nowadays.

The Seal " rookeries," as they are called, are a great sight.
Do any of my readers remember Mr. Kipling's description of one
of them, in his delightful *Jungle Book* ?   This is how he pictures
the place and its " people."

" Now that all the Seals and their wives were on the land, you
could hear their clamour miles out to sea above the loudest gales.
At the lowest counting there were over a million Seals on the
beach—old Seals, mother Seals, tiny babies, and holluschickie,
fighting, scuffling, bleating, crawling, and playing together—going
down to the sea and coming up from it in gangs and regiments,
lying over every foot of ground as far as the eye could reach, and
skirmishing about in brigades through the fog."

And this picture, too, of the life lived there by a baby Seal :
" He paddled and scrambled about by his mother's side, and
learned to scuffle out of the way when his father was fighting
with another Seal, and the two rolled and roared up and down
the slippery rocks. . . . The first thing he did was to crawl inland,
and there he met tens of thousands of babies of his own age, and
they played together like puppies, went to sleep on the clean sand,
and played again.   The old people on the nurseries took no notice
of them, and the holluschickie kept to their own grounds, and the
babies had a beautiful play-time."

Seals captured when fairly young can be taught all manner
of really clever tricks ; and if taken when they are babies they have
been known to become as much attached to their owners as
dogs.

Many are the stories told of these pet Seals.   Here is one which I
give in brief : A boy living on one of the wilder parts of our northern
coasts had a baby Seal given to him by some fishermen.   It was
about a fortnight old, and in a few weeks it was perfectly tame ;
followed him about, ate from his hand, and showed evident
pleasure whenever his master drew near.   " It was fond of
heat, and would lie for hours at the kitchen fire."   It would

nestle close to the dogs, who soon got used to their strange new companion.

But when the winter came on the supply of fish grew scarce, for the boats were often unable to put out. So the Seal had to go short, and soon milk had to be given it instead. But it drank so much that the boy's parents decided that the animal could not be kept any longer. So he and a friend rowed out a couple of miles from shore, one day, and gently dropped the Seal overboard.

But instead of frisking with delight and diving out of sight, the poor animal showed great distress at being left. It swam after the boat with cries so pitiful that at last the rowers stopped pulling and lifted the creature in, and took it home once more. Of course it became a greater favourite than ever, and there was no more talk of " getting rid of it."

The amount of fish that a full-grown Seal consumes in a day is very large. Ten pounds is the lowest reckoning. And it seems that, like the otter, a Seal will often take a single bite out of a big fish—the part he likes best. Indeed, I fancy he would starve if he became a land creature and lived on land food : only the inexhaustible ocean can provide enough daily food for animals with such a huge appetite.

The teeth of a Seal are just adapted for catching and holding such slippery prey. Besides the long canine teeth, which all flesh-eating animals have, its other teeth are very sharp and run to points of different sizes, so that wriggle as he may the poor fish has no chance of getting away.

There are many kinds of Seals ; some of them have peculiarities of form, some of colour-markings.

There is the Sea-Lion of Patagonia and of the Pribyloff Islands, which, if it is a male, has a tawny mane about its neck, and is a really big fellow, often measuring ten and even twelve feet in length, and weighing 1000 lbs.

Then there is the Grey Seal, which sometimes visits the British and the Irish coasts, and finds its way up into lochs in the Highlands where there is a water-way to the sea. The Common Seal may very likely have been seen by my English readers, though it is more abundant on the Scottish coast.

The Harp Seal belongs to the Arctic regions, and is there hunted for the oil to be got from it ; it is not a fur Seal.

The Bladder-nosed Seal is so called because of the curious air-bag which covers the head and nose of the male. Now, as the sealers always find that a blow struck on the nose of a Seal stuns it instantly, the Bladder-Nose is better off than its fellows, for the air-bag is almost as good as a helmet. And there is a great deal of the fighting-man about these Seals. Not only do they fight among themselves during the marrying season, the jealous males biting and screaming at one another most spitefully ; but they do not hesitate to attack men if angered. And the rush of a Bladder-Nose, with its gleaming teeth, is not a thing to be laughed at.

This is the Seal which more than any other is hunted by the Eskimo. I have already mentioned many of the uses to which that bold little hunter and fisherman is able to put his capture.

Even more odd-looking is the Elephant Seal, with its strange snout. It is a huge beast, often measuring over twenty feet in length. Fifty years ago there were thousands of these giants on certain favourite beaches far away in the Antarctic seas, but the numbers have been sadly thinned by the bludgeons of ships' crews, and in many places the harmless creatures are now extinct.

THE WALRUS.

WE can hardly think of the great black sprawling Walrus as anywhere but in the Arctic Ocean with its fields of ice, and its solitudes, and its bitter cold.

Yet before the arch-enemy man came killing and scaring them away to those dreary regions, the seals and the Walrus sunned themselves by thousands on the shingle and rocks of the northern parts of Europe.

Do you remember the poem in which Longfellow tells how—

> "Othere, the old sea-captain
>   Who dwelt in Helgoland,
> To King Alfred, the Lover of Truth,
> Brought a snow-white walrus tooth,
>   Which he held in his brown right hand."

He relates to the king the story of how he sailed northward, further and further, till he reached and rounded the headland which we call the North Cape, where at Midsummer there is no night, for the sunlight never fades out of the sky.

> "And there we hunted the walrus,
>   The narwhale and the seal;
> Ha! 'Twas a noble game!
> And like the lightning's flame
>   Flew our harpoons of steel.
>
> There were six of us altogether,
>   Norsemen of Helgoland;
> In two days, and no more,
> We killed of them threescore,
>   And dragged them to the strand!"

And when King Alfred stopped writing down the story, doubting if such things were true, the bronzed old seafarer triumphantly held out the white ivory he had brought away in token of what he had seen and done in that distant sea.

The two strong canine teeth of the Walrus grow to such a length that they cannot be shut inside the mouth. The possession of these tusks distinguishes their owner from all his relatives in the great seal family : he is quite one by himself.

These tusks, which sometimes measure as much as two feet in length, are ivory worth fetching from far away. Not that Nature thought of the prices they would obtain in the city auction-room, when she lengthened these two teeth in the great seal's head. She did this to enable him to rout about on the sea-floor, and vary his meals of fish and shrimps with a feast of cockles and mussels, not forgetting a dessert of seaweed. The long chisel-like tusks enable him to tear these latter dainties from the rocks and sea-bed.

He uses them, too, as a mountaineer sometimes uses his ice-axe, striking them into the slippery ice at some rather too steep landing-place, and hauling himself up by alternately using his strong flippers and these reliable hold-fasts. For he is a clumsy creature at the best.

Captain Cook, the great navigator, who lived at a time when the Walrus was generally thought of as rather a terrible monster, gave a very different report. "They lie in herds of many hundreds on the ice," he wrote, "huddling over one another like swine. In fact, they lie just like a lot of pigs in a yard."

Even when they were fired at, the flash of the gunpowder in the old-fashioned muskets seemed enough to scatter them.

Not always are they so easily scared, however. An American writer thus tells of his own experience. He and his boat's crew had gone out to get shots at a herd which they had seen lying about on a "raft" of floating ice. They had crept up almost unnoticed, and fired, hitting three of the Walrus. At the noise one and all of them slid into the water, and two sank (a Walrus usually sinks when killed, unless held up by a harpoon line), but a harpoon was skilfully lodged in the broad back of the third one hit.

Says the writer : "In a few minutes the whole herd appeared at the surface [they had dived instantly], about fifty yards away from us, the harpooned animal being among them. In a few moments we were completely surrounded by them.

"That they meant to attack us was now clear. They seemed to want to get their tusks over the gunwale of the boat. And we knew that if one of the monsters did hook on to us in this way, the boat would be torn in pieces, and we should be left floating in the sea helpless."

The crew struck and pushed back the intruders as well as they

THE WALRUS.

[*Drawn by* Joseph Wolf.

could with their oars, and the three gunners loaded and fired as quickly as possible ; but it was in the days of the old-fashioned rifle, in which the powder had to be rammed home each time.

Suddenly an immense Walrus, with enormously long tusks, was seen to be pushing his way through the herd, with mouth open, bellowing dreadfully. "The monster, his head high above the boat, was less than a yard away when I fired point-blank, and he went down like a stone.

"This ended the battle ; I do not know why, but the whole

herd seemed then to take alarm, and all dived down with a tremendous splash almost at the same moment."

But the harpooned animal was secured, and drawn in to the edge of the ice, where it could be dealt with.

It had been rather a sharp scare for the writer, who had always thought the Walrus was not a beast for man to be very much afraid of.

In an old magazine for January 1868, I came upon this interesting note of a " new arrival " at the Zoo :

" A visitor from the northern seas has come among us. The Zoological Society has just received a young Walrus captured in Davis Straits. A boat's crew landed on the ice to attack a herd of some two or three hundred. They killed a large female Walrus, which was fastened to the boat and towed towards the ship. A young male Walrus followed the body, refusing to leave his dead parent. Having got a noose over his head, the sailors hauled him on board. He was fastened on deck, but refused food for some days ; at last he swallowed some thin slips of boiled pork, and thus he was fed till the ship reached home.

" He is about eight feet long, and weighs perhaps two and a half hundredweight. It is to be hoped he will be made comfortable, and take to his new quarters, as this is the only healthy animal of the sort the Zoo has ever received."

I think I am right in guessing that this was the Walrus which is spoken of by Mr. Bartlett, the late superintendent of the Zoo, in one of his books. He mentions going to Dundee in the autumn of 1867 to see a young Walrus which had been brought home by a whaling ship. He paid £200 for it, and it came to London with him by steamer.

He says : " Its food was chiefly mussels and clams, which I got from Yorkshire. It would feed on whiting and cod, cut up without the bones. This animal lived only about four months."

About this little stranger from the Arctic Seas he tells an amusing story.

As its tusks were not properly grown, he, Mr. Bartlett, put the skull of a full-grown Walrus in the yard where this youngster spent much of its time. People could thus see what a size the young Walrus might grow to.

One day Mr. Bartlett noticed a visitor thoughtfully staring first at the latter and then at the skull. He had seen in country parks the old antlers of deer lying about; for deer shed their horns at certain seasons. The man was much perplexed. At last he turned to Mr. Bartlett who was passing by, and said, " Mister, did he really *shed that skull* ? "

THE BEARS.

BEARS are the clowns of the Animal World. Their little twinkling eyes, their fat sides and lazy shuffling gait, the way they tumble about without hurting themselves, their ungainly gambols, and the real sense of fun which most of them display, mark them out as creatures whom we ought to laugh at and feel kindly disposed towards, rather than distrust and fear.

Despite his sharp teeth and blunt powerful claws and terrible hug, the world has had a sort of good-humoured liking for the funny, padding, shambling beast, which it has felt for very few of the dangerous animals. Fairy tales and nursery tales are a good test—how does the bear figure in them? The wolf is always the treacherous beast, the fox the sly, clever beast, but the Bear is the slow, comfortable, easy-going fellow who does not want to do harm to any one.

With some few exceptions the Bear in real life lives up to this pleasant character. The great claws can indeed rend and tear a foe, but they are mostly in use for digging up roots, climbing, and suchlike peaceful occupations. The sharp teeth are seldom used for tearing up flesh-food. Down that red throat that can send out such fearsome roars, honey and fruit, grubs and berries pass far more frequently than fresh-killed meat.

Even the terrible Grizzly Bear of North America is as fond of dead fish, seemingly, as of anything. It is only the Ice Bear who comes near to being a flesh-eater and nothing else, and he, poor fellow, has but little choice in the question, for he lives in a world where there are no fruit trees, and where the humming of bees is never heard. But even he is a vegetarian when he can find such food. During the short Arctic summer he has been seen grazing, like a great sheep, on the short moss and herbage which may be found on many of the slopes and hillsides at that season.

Our ancestors knew the Bear and his habits quite well. An old book written in the Middle Ages thus quaintly describes him: " He can wonderly sty (climb wonderfully) upon trees unto the highest tops of them, and oft bees gather honey in hollow trees, and the Bear findeth honey by smell, and goeth up to the place that the honey is in, and maketh a way into the tree with his claws, and draweth out the honey and eateth it, and cometh oft by custom unto such a place when he is an-hungered."

Those Bears that live in countries where the coming of winter means great cold and perhaps scarcity of food, make snug winter quarters for themselves by clearing a space under the roots of some great tree, or by heaping up moss and dead leaves and the like in some dense thicket, or cave, or rocky cleft, and burrowing into it.

There the animal lies in the sleep or torpor of what is called hibernation. The warmth of the spring sunshine wakes him, and out he crawls, blinking and dazed, and very thin indeed. For, all that time, a Bear "lives on his own fat," and the supply is pretty well used up. Happily for him, the sun that has called him from sleep has already been drawing out the leafbuds on the trees and bushes, and rousing the bees to their winged errands, and the ants to their busy coming and going in the warm soil. Food will be more plentiful in a few weeks' time, but meanwhile there is enough to satisfy a moderate Bear appetite. And five months of solid sleep must be enough for any animal even of Bruin's size.

Of Bears there are many kinds. It will be better to speak of them each in turn—at least of the chief members of the family.

The one with which we are most familiar is

THE BROWN BEAR.

He is often seen in England, but only as a visitor from abroad. The dusty-coated "performing Bears" which are led about the country at the end of a chain are mostly from the Pyrenees or from the rugged lands that lie between Austria and Turkey.

But long ago Great Britain also was the home of the Brown

Bear. There was plenty of room for wild animals of his size then, in the mighty forests, south and north. They were there when the Roman legionaries marched over hill and dale, "conquering and to conquer." The wolf and the Bear must have seen the glint of their armour as they went by.

Some of the Bears, we know, were caught and caged, and shipped across the Channel to be shown to the people at Rome, in those cruel and wasteful exhibitions in the blood-stained amphitheatre. The great Caledonian Forest sheltered many huge specimens. One of these Scottish Bears is mentioned by a Roman poet of the time as being let loose on a condemned robber, Laureolus by name, as he hung fastened to a cross—a truly dreadful death.

It is not quite certain when the last of the British Bears was hunted down and killed—most likely it was before William the Conqueror came over—but the swift and cunning wolf long survived his clumsy forest neighbour.

On the Continent, however, Bears still hold their own in the wilder parts of many countries.

The mountains are the Bear's chief stronghold. In the High Alps he is now rarely seen except in winter, but he *is* there, albeit his numbers grow less as his haunts are more and more invaded. A few years ago, I was told by an innkeeper at Trafoi, on the great Stelvio Pass, that one Sunday morning, the previous winter, a she-Bear and two cubs made their way down the hillside out of the thick woods. He thought they must be dogs, but soon saw his mistake and rushed indoors for his gun; for in frost-time Bears are apt to "go for" the goats if they themselves are awake and hungry. The old Bear in this case was shot, but the cubs made off, and got clear away.

The long mountain range of the Carpathians, Mount Pindus, on the northern borders of Greece, the Balkan States, and the wilder parts of Sweden and Norway—in all these places the Brown Bear has his home.

But, above all, he belongs to Russia. In the boundless forests of that vast country, especially Northern Russia, where no disturbing sound invades except perhaps the sound of the wood-man's axe, or sleigh bells on the lonely post road that runs through the solitude, he finds all he requires for a happy life. Here many of his tribe grow to an immense size.

The poor peasants make a little money now and then in winter, by tracking them to their sleeping-places and sending word to some well-to-do sportsman that they have a Bear for him to shoot. They sometimes earn more money in this way than by months of labour in the fields.

In Russia every one who is at all well-to-do wears furs, and the soft long-haired fur of the Bear is in much request. The supply is not likely to be exhausted for many years to come, as, besides Russia in Europe, the great stretch of territory which we may call Russian Asia is also the home of the great Brown Bear.

This Bear has been tamed often enough, and we all know what an obedient pupil he becomes; but there are stories which show him in a very pleasant light even while he is in a wild state.

Atkinson, the writer of a book on Siberia, tells us of two little children who wandered into the forest. Their anxious parents went in search, and found them playing with a large Bear. The great creature seemed to be delighted with his new companions, one of whom was seen to be feeding him with fruit, while the other had scrambled on his back, and was holding on by his shaggy coat. At the frightened cry of the parents the Bear quietly slipped away and trundled off into the forest.

The rough-and-tumble antics of Bear cubs at play with each other, or of the mother with her children, are a most amusing sight, but it is one not often seen except in captivity, the Bear's hearing being quick to catch an approaching footfall.

Bears were kept in this country long before the present "Zoo" was established. The cruel sport of Bear-baiting was carried on here for hundreds of years: the Bear being chained to a post, and then set upon by bulldogs.

In an old book full of quaint lore collected several

THE BROWN BEAR.

hundred years ago occurs this reference to captive Bears : " When he is taken he is made blind with a bright basin, and bound with chains, and compelled to play, and tamed with beating ; and is an unsteadfast beast, and unstable and uneasy, and goeth therefore all day about the stake, to the which he is strongly tied."

A much happier existence is enjoyed by the Bears which are kept in England nowadays. Those that are led up and down the country by foreigners wishing to make a little money, seem, for the most part, to be kindly treated. And as for those at the Zoological Gardens in London, they have a very pleasant time indeed.

The late Mr. Bartlett, Superintendent of the Zoo, used to tell a good story of the way in which one Bear came into his possession.

Two strolling Frenchmen who had been leading about a large Bear, in and around London, made their way down to Brentford. Here, through the fussiness of a nervous old lady, they came to loggerheads with the police. They knew no English, and the policeman knew no French. A misunderstanding easily arose.

The two poor foreigners were brought before the magistrate, charged with creating a disturbance. They were sentenced to imprisonment for a month, and the Bear was ordered to be taken charge of " for the safety of the public." It was decided to send the great beast to the London Zoo.

But how to send him was another thing. He scratched and growled at any one who tried to touch him. At last he was half-coaxed, half-forced *into an omnibus*. The door was slammed and locked, and the driver whipped up his horses. But the Bear (surely he must have enjoyed the whole affair as much as a refractory schoolboy !) quietly got out at the window, careless of the broken glass, which could not hurt his shaggy skin, and coolly stopped the bus by hanging, with all his weight, on to the hind-wheel. He would have dropped to the ground and made off altogether, but his chain prevented that.

There was nothing to be done but to go back to Brentford and ask the two poor Frenchmen to come out of prison and help get their unmanageable pet conveyed safely to London. Truly a very funny side to a serious story !

Perhaps there is no place in the world where the Brown Bear

"ALWAYS READY."

A STUDY AT THE ZOO.

is more in evidence than the city of Berne in Switzerland. The city, indeed, gets its name from the Swabian word for Bear. The story of the killing of a huge Bear by Duke Berthold v., the founder of Berne, in 1191, is an old legend which may have had its rise in the fact that this animal was the duke's crest.

Be that as it may, the figure of the Bear is everywhere in Berne, even to-day. It is carved by thousands in all sizes, and in many attitudes; here and there it is seen beside the ancient statues that decorate the quaint old streets; and—most interesting of all—there is the Bear-pit, on the eastern side of the city, which for hundreds of years has been one of the sights of Berne.

Early in the 18th century an old lady left a fortune to be spent in keeping up this Bear-pit. But years went by, and war broke out. The armies of Napoleon overran Switzerland; the money, which by that time amounted to the great sum of nearly £80,000, was carried off by the conquerors; and the city Bears were transferred to the Jardin des Plantes, the Zoological Gardens of Paris.

When peace at last returned, the citizens of Berne subscribed to buy a fresh lot of Bears, and provided a sum for their upkeep.

THE SYRIAN BEAR.

This is the Bear of Old Testament story. We may look upon it as being only a variety of the common Brown Bear of Europe. It is still found, though in very diminished numbers, in the lonelier parts of Palestine, and the Lebanon—the mountain country to the north, once famous for its great cedars ; also in the Caucasus, and, some say, as far eastward as Northern Persia.

SYRIAN BEAR, AT THE ZOOLOGICAL GARDENS.

The Syrian Bear of to-day is not a very formidable-looking beast, and is much smaller than, say, the Russian Bear.   But from what we read in the Bible it would seem that the creature was once held in very great respect indeed.

My readers will readily recall the story of the " children " (young people, as we should say) who mocked Elisha, and the strange punishment that befell them : " There came forth two she-Bears out of the wood, and tare forty and two of them." David, speaking to King Saul, proudly mentions, as a proof of his courage, that he had fought and killed both a lion and a Bear, in defence of his father's flock. And there are quite a number of texts which refer to the ferocious temper of a Bear robbed of its cubs, as if nothing could be more terrifying.

But Bears need cover, and the thickets and forests that once clothed the hills and ravines of Central Palestine have disappeared. Their old haunts are now bare, dry, sun-scorched wastes, and so they have retreated to the mountainous districts further north.

Twenty or thirty years ago they were quite common on Mount Hermon. One traveller speaks of seeing a pair of them rolling over one another in the snow, at the close of a summer's day, and enjoying it much as a boy enjoys a cold plunge at the end of a long hot walk.

The charcoal-burners living on or close to the mountain seemed so used to the sight of Bears that they were surprised at the excited interest shown by their English visitor. And the owners of the cultivated fields at the foot of the mountain regarded the Bear simply as a nuisance. For he had a great liking for certain of their crops—lentils especially, and grapes and other fruit—and was in the habit of making his way down towards them from the high rocks, after sunset.

THE GRIZZLY BEAR.

Half a century ago, when great tracts of North America had not heard the sound of the axe, much less that of the locomotive, the Grizzly Bear was no uncommon sight to the hunter and trapper.

That great continent has three Bears of its own—the Black

Bear, the Brown Bear (of America), and the Grizzly. The first is an expert climber, and greedy of honey, the second is much like its European namesake, and the third is the most formidable and most dreaded of them all.

The backwoodsmen of old days had good reason to beware of " Old Ephraim," as they called him, and stories of the most exciting kind used to be told round the camp-fire about the hair-breadth escapes which they, or men they had known, had had from this huge beast.

His size alone was enough to compel respect. Eight feet long from nose to tail was no unusual measurement for a full-grown specimen ; and nine feet has on several occasions been recorded. As the animal often measures nearly as much round the body, and frequently turns the scale at 800 lbs., we can readily understand that for a hunter to find himself without firearms face to face with an irate Grizzly is to feel that his last hour has probably come.

Despite its weight and size, the animal hurls itself at its foe with amazing swiftness. An ox would go down before such a charge ; much more easily a man. Indeed, a single blow from one of those enormously broad and powerful paws will knock a man senseless ; and if those terrible talons, which frequently measure five inches long, are brought into play, the wounds thus inflicted are very dreadful ones, especially if they strike the head and face, as so often they do.

Many a hunter thus attacked has come off with his life by remembering one strange habit of his huge opponent. This is, to stop mauling his victim when he believes he has killed him, and, dragging him to a shallow trench or hollow which he has dug with his great claws, to bury him for a few hours, shovelling earth and leaves upon the living grave and patting them down.

Knowing this, the victim has often feigned death, and as soon as the Bear has gone away or lain down to sleep, has scrambled out and made his way off.

It is said that other animals, both wild and tame, have a most incurable dread of the Grizzly.

The trapper's pack-horse will shy and whinny with terror when the pelt (skin) of one is thrown across the saddle. This

TURNING THE TABLES.

GRIZZLY BEAR PURSUED BY CATTLE.

[*Drawn by* FREDERICK BURTON.

fear is well founded, for a Grizzly will often launch itself against a passing horse whether its rider is on its back or not. It is said that wolves will shrink from touching the carcase of a dead Grizzly.

As for the Indians, who roamed through the haunts of the Grizzly long before the white man came with his better weapons and his bigger knowledge, they regarded even his dead form as they might the dwelling-place of a powerful and revengeful spirit. And so in their superstitious way they soothed the spirit of the Bear with flattering words.

In those old days the Grizzly was to be found almost from end to end of the North American continent—or, to be more exact, from Mexico to the northern ranges of the Rocky Mountains. But, as in the case of the bison, and the beaver, and the sea otter, and many another animal, the coming of the white man has almost meant extirpation for him. One day, not very far hence, the Grizzly Bear will have to be sought for either in Zoo collections, or in those preserved open spaces in which the American nation is trying to save many of its wild creatures from extinction. Even there it may be found difficult to preserve him, on account of his dangerous ways.

The Bears which to-day come sniffing round the dust-heaps of the hotels in the great Yellowstone Park are not Grizzlies, though tourists like to call them so. It is only in certain remote districts that the true Grizzly is now to be met with.

The London Zoo has had one or more specimens of the Grizzly Bear for many years past, though now and then the cage is empty and a fresh specimen has to be obtained.

Bears in captivity have their troubles as well as their wild comrades in the mountain forests of the West. One of these is a tendency to go blind. A cataract (a kind of film or skin) is apt to form over the eyeball, till the poor beast can no longer see. Sometimes both eyes are thus affected.

One would fancy that it would be most difficult, not to say impossible, to cure a Bear as a human patient is cured. But this has been done. The case occurred a good many years ago, one of the most celebrated eye-doctors of the day being called in to operate.

The first part of the task was the most puzzling—how to get

17

the great creature near enough to the bars of his cage for the surgeon to reach the eyes. This at last was managed; a leather collar with a stout chain attached to it was fastened round his neck, and he was then hauled—it took four men to do it !—to the front of his den. A sponge full of chloroform was tied to his nose, and the powerful fumes soon overcame him. When next he awoke and scrambled sleepily to his feet, the operation was over, the cataract had been cleared from his eyes, and he could see as well as any Bear in the Zoo.

THE MALAYAN SUN-BEAR.

This is one of the smaller Bears. He and his tribe are to be found in Borneo, Sumatra, and the spice-scented island of Java, as well as in the long forest-clad peninsula after which it is named.

There is another Sun-Bear in Thibet, that mysterious land which was for so long shut off from the world by its mountains, and by the jealous fear which its people had of strangers. But the Thibetan Sun-Bear with its shaggy cheeks is markedly different, though it has the regular Sun-Bear badge of white on its chest.

Perhaps the chief thing to be said about the Malayan Sun-Bear is that, whether wild or captive, its appetite is enormous. It is equally partial to honey and fruit, and Nature has given it special powers for getting as much as it desires of both. The tongue can be stretched out and elongated, much like that of the giraffe, and thereby it can worm itself into the honeycomb and lick the honey out of every corner and crevice, in a way which would be impossible to an ordinary Bear's tongue. Even the lips, they say, can be shot out in a most unusual manner.

As for fruit-gathering, it can climb, like most of its clan, and should it wish to bring the fruit and berries to the ground, it has such long strong claws and powerful arms that it can clasp and uproot even trees of considerable size. It is said that the damage these Bears will do among the cocoa-nut trees is immense ; the tender shoots especially being sought after by them, to the ruin of the tree.

At the Zoo the Malayan Sun-Bear is popular. People like his odd ways, and his unfailing readiness to come forward and be fed. Not long ago a visitor, talking with one of the keepers about the appetite of Bears, had an illustration given him there and then.

One of these Sun-Bears had been fed by the public on and off all day, besides having his regular meals. At the close of the day the keeper set to work to see whether there was any falling off in the appetite of his glossy-coated charge. He tried him with ship's biscuits. Nine of these very substantial dainties disappeared one after the other down the Sun-Bear's throat. The tenth was eaten a little less eagerly. It was getting near his bed-time, and he was somewhat tired. But he consumed seven more, and it was not until the eighteenth biscuit had followed the rest that the little gourmand shut both his mouth and his eyes, and composed himself to sleep. He made the morrow a fast day—as well he might—but on the third day he was himself again.

Sir Stamford Raffles, who did so much to build up our Empire in the East, a century ago, and spent the best years of his life in the Malay Peninsula, was very much interested in this native species of Bear, and wrote a great deal that was new and interesting about its ways and peculiarities.

He himself had one in his Eastern home. It was so gentle and quiet that it was allowed to play with the children. It never had to be tied up, nor punished for any spiteful or mischievous act, but was allowed just to roam at will about the house and grounds. Unlike so many favoured pets it was not jealous of the other four-footed or feathered playmates, but would feed with them in the friendliest manner.

Its odd ways greatly amused visitors to the house. It had a habit of sitting bolt upright, thrusting out its long flexible tongue till the onlooker wondered how ever much more was coming, and then sharply drawing it back into its mouth with a flick like the snap of a whip-lash. But, like all its species, it was a most restless little creature.

THE POLAR BEAR.

He is king of " the white North," with none to withstand him. Only man, when he comes to the inhospitable regions which are the Ice Bear's home, can face and slay him.

His strength and size are immense. Seven feet long from muzzle to tail is no uncommon measurement; a length of ten and even eleven feet has been known. And in the dreary wilderness of the Polar ice-fields giants of even greater size may possibly exist.

As befits so large a beast, who has to catch and kill his own food, his coat is the colour of his surroundings—all except his nose-tip and his claws. The latter are well-nigh hidden in the long white fur, and the former he often contrives to conceal, when he is out hunting, in a way which is droll in its cunning intelligence. So that when at last he springs upon his prey, it must seem to the victim as if part of the snowy ground, on which it has been unsuspiciously resting, had risen up and taken shape.

The seal is his chief prey, but seals cannot be caught every day—especially if he has scared them by too persistent pursuit; so he makes up with fish, large and small. To catch the latter, it is plain, he must have lightning quickness; but to capture, nay, even to get near, the shy, suspicious seal, he must use his wits as well as move quickly.

His acute sense of smell helps him. By it he can detect the tiny breathing-hole in the ice which betrays the unseen presence of a seal. And by his extraordinary swimming powers he makes it almost as difficult for his victim to escape by water as by land. To us it seems a marvellous thing that a man should have been able to swim, as did Captain Webb, across the Channel, from Dover to Calais, but the Ice Bear has been seen " going strong " across a channel which was nearly forty miles wide. Indeed, it is recorded that one was seen on one occasion swimming easily an even greater distance out to sea, and with no floating ice-raft anywhere near to suggest that he had been carried part of the way.

Huge and cumbrous as they appear to be on land, Polar Bears are " light as corks " in the water, and seem as much at home, floating and swimming and diving, as when they are trundling across some ice-field or climbing the sloping sides of some great berg.

Altogether it will be seen that from the point of view of the other Arctic animals the Ice Bear is a veritable terror. The seal can never feel safe for five minutes together. Even the huge unwieldy Walrus is liable to be pounced on, though it goes hard

POLAR BEARS AT THE ZOO.

with Bruin if his victim's long sharp tusks can reach and gore him.

Even man himself was held in contempt by him, until the last fifty years or so, during which the hunting rifle has been perfected. In the olden times when a man's only weapon was a club or a spear things were much more equal, and it was only the boldest spirits that would await the charge of an angry Bear in his native ice-fields.

Early voyagers brought back to Europe accounts of his size, his strength, his ferocity. In a very old book, there is a reference to the Bears that then were to be found as far south as Iceland :

" Also in that region are White Bears most great and right fierce ; that break ice with their claws, and make many holes therein, and dive there-through into the sea, and take fish under the ice, and draw them out through the same holes, and bring them to the cliff and live thereby."

The explorer Cabot, who discovered Newfoundland, gives a very similar description : " Plunging themselves into the water where they perceive a multitude of these fishes to lie, they fasten their claws in their scales, and so draw them to land and eat them ; so that the Bears, being thus satisfied with fish, are not noisome (hurtful or dangerous) to men."

Nearly ninety years later Captain John Davis—who has given his name to the Straits which divide Greenland from the far north-east of North America—sailed up into these icy waters with two tiny ships. One landing-party speedily fell in with Bears. A huge fellow, with feet fourteen inches broad, was surprised asleep on the highest part of an island. The men shot at him with their clumsy matchlocks ; but even with several bullets in him he clutched fiercely at the sharp spears that were levelled at him, and tried to escape by swimming. But Davis's men made after him, and killed and took him.

Then came Barents the Dutchman, and he and his men, too, had cause to remember the Bears. For one of the seamen, loitering behind the others, as they explored a certain island, was caught and mauled so badly that he died. His comrades attacked the monster with their spears, but it was not till a loaded musket was fetched from the ship that Bruin was slain. His skin was about the only valuable thing that the luckless adventurers brought back with them to Amsterdam.

With the gradual improvement of firearms the White Bear became less formidable, until, at the present day, the prowling of Bears round the camp is regarded more as a nuisance than a danger—so deadly a weapon is the modern rifle in hands trained to use it.

Of course, exciting adventures with Polar Bears are still

THE POLAR BEAR.

[*Drawn by* GEORGE RANKIN.

numerous enough, but as we read of them we do not seem to have the feeling of " fighting fearful odds " as must have been the case in the old days.

But if we want to know what Bear hunting was like when there were no firearms, we must join an Eskimo hunting-party. A generation ago, Dr. Kane described such an experience.

He says : " The tracks of Bears were becoming more and more numerous as we rounded one iceberg after another ; and we could see the beds they had worn in the snow while watching for seal. These diverted the dogs from their course, and they suddenly came upon a large male Bear in the act of devouring a seal. The impulse was irresistible. I lost all control over both dogs and drivers ; they seemed dead to everything except the eager wish to pursue. Off they sped with incredible swiftness, the Eskimo clinging to their sledges, and cheering their dogs with loud cries of ' Nannook ! ' "

He tells us how well the dogs are trained to help in the hunt. They are taught to bother and distract the Bear, and hinder him if he turns tail and makes off, but not to actually attack him.

When the trail of a Bear is found, and the dogs "laid on" to it, (harnessed of course, as they are, to the usual light sleigh), their master drives at a brisk pace across the snow until they come in sight of their quarry. Bruin looks round, much startled, sniffs the air as he raises himself on his haunches, and takes to flight.

Then the driver leans over the side of his rushing sleigh, and unfastens two of the team. Yelping joyously the two dogs rush on ahead, and coming up with their adversary they so worry him that he turns at bay.

Then up come their comrades in harness, wild with excitement. The traces are slipped off, and the whole pack swarms round the Bear. In a few moments his attention is so entirely taken up with the bites of his yelping, snapping tormentors, that the Eskimo gets the chance he has waited for. He darts forward, and in an instant has driven his sharp lance into Bruin's left side, just below the shoulder.

Soon the dead monster is cut up, master and dogs gorge

themselves with the flesh, till they can eat no more ; and the rest of the meat is buried in the snow.

Bear's flesh, by the bye, is thought not to be wholesome for human beings ; but every explorer is glad to have it for his dogs, for if they cannot be properly fed and their strength kept up, it means that he and his comrades will have to pull the sleighs themselves. This is most exhausting work, especially if the ice-fields are rough and rugged.

Great is the curiosity of the Polar Bear. Unless he has learned by dearly bought experience that the coming of man means the coming of danger, he will wander sniffing round the camp of the explorer. And if he sees a ship at anchor off the coast he will often swim out to it, and his white head with its black muzzle will be noticed by the watch on deck, bobbing up and down as he paddles round the mysterious monster that has come into his native waters.

The same inquisitiveness leads to his digging into abandoned huts, piles of wreckage, or buried stores of provisions. The latter trick is a most tiresome one, for the next expedition that comes along may be depending on this supply of food thus carefully concealed and preserved under the snow.

Bears that roam about the coasts of those inhospitable lands, sometimes wake up from a long nap to find that the patch of snow-covered ground on which they had lain down to sleep is really only floating ice, and has broken off from the rest of the floe. If the cake of ice has drifted a long way from shore, Bruin may decide not to jump off and swim to land. And so the ice-floe moves out into the ocean with its strange freight.

Dr. Scoresby mentions the case of a Bear which he met floating along at a distance of 200 miles from the nearest land. Poor lonely voyager ! unless he soon strands on some new shore, or can manage to espy and catch a passing fish, his fate is likely to be the terrible one of death by starvation.

Bear cubs, whose parents have been shot, are often brought back by whaling ships and others, and some of them find their way to wild beast shows, small and great. Their fur is apt to have become very yellow on board ship, but it regains its proper whiteness ere long.

POLAR BEAR ADRIFT ON AN ICE-FLOE.

[*Drawn by* GEORGE RANKIN.

The White Bear at the Zoo is always an object of interest, and when he dies his successor is not long in arriving to fill the vacant place. One which was supplied to the Gardens by some Dundee whalers, half a century ago, had been kept in a cask only some five and a half feet long, for more than three months, on board ship. Poor prisoner, how he must have enjoyed being transferred even to a walled enclosure after such cramped quarters !

It has been noticed, as a strange fact, that in such places as the London Zoo, and the Thiergarten at Hamburg, the Polar Bears

THE POLAR BEAR.　　　[*Drawn by* JOSEPH WOLF.

seem not only to suffer less from the hot summer sun than other captive animals, but even to enjoy it. One scorching day Carl Hagenbeck, the owner of the Thiergarten, walking round the " Gardens," found one of the tigers and one of the leopards faint and prostrate with the heat, while the white-clad visitor from the regions of snow and ice was so delighted with the burning glare that it had come out from the cool shadow of its inner cage and stretched itself out on the sun-baked flagstones to enjoy the blazing heat.

Before there was a Zoo in London, many wild beasts were kept at the Tower. A fine Grizzly Bear, which had been presented to King George III. by the Hudson Bay Company, was quartered here. And centuries earlier still there was a White Bear which had been given to Henry III. In an old record we find that the Sheriffs of London were ordered, by royal command, to spend fourpence a day (this represented a very much larger sum in those days) in providing food for this Bear and his keeper. They were also instructed to provide a long and strong cord to fasten round him while he bathed in the river Thames ; a muzzle and an iron chain were also to be part of his equipment.

And when Queen Elizabeth went in state through Spitalfields, in 1559, with a glittering escort of a thousand men-at-arms, and much beating of drums and sounding of trumpets, two " features " in the procession delighted the populace. These were a pair of morris dancers with their strange antics, and a cart in which were two Polar Bears.

THE WOLF.

IT is many a day since the long-drawn howl of the Wolf made the faces of English women and children turn pale with fear. But the name of that fierce and snarling beast still means much even to English ears—a ferocious foe, a fleet-footed robber, a terror of the night.

The wolf stands for many things that are hateful, and for nothing that is good. He has neither the nobleness of the lion nor the drollery of the bear. Nor is he at heart a peace-lover, like so many even of the dangerous animals, unless it be when he finds himself outmatched, and would be glad to get away.

We who live in this happy island should be thankful that the day of the Wolf in Great Britain is over. He was hunted down at last. And because there was no way of escaping from this country, it was only a matter of time for the last one to be slain.

For, on the Continent, when Wolves are hard pressed they can often make their way over the frontier to another country. Moreover, their numbers can always be replenished by others which come stealing in from the great forest-lands of Russia.

So the British Wolf, like the British reindeer that once browsed on the desolate hills of Caithness, the British beaver that was once busy on Welsh and Yorkshire streams, the British bear that lived on into Saxon times, and the wild boar that disappeared somewhere about the time when King Charles the Second " enjoyed his own again," found himself cornered at last, and knew " the game was up."

Before I pass on to speak of Wolves in the lands they inhabit to-day, you boys and girls may like to hear something of the British Wolf and the traditions about him which have come down to us.

When once you have pictured this island of ours as it was in

271

Saxon times, with its enormous forests of oak and beech and ash, stretching away for thirty, fifty, seventy miles perhaps, with scarcely a break ; when you remember how few roads ran through these forests, except those made, and made so well, by the conquering Romans ; and when you think how little traffic there was along these highways except at certain seasons of the year, you will not wonder at the way in which such strong, swift creatures held their own, year after year and century after century.

So numerous were they, and so bold in their attacks at the beginning of the year, when the cold was most severe and their usual food most scarce, that our Saxon forefathers called the month of January, Wolf Month.

Not only in the northern half of our island, where we should expect them to be found, but all over England it would seem, Wolves lurked and prowled. Herdsmen and travellers alike were always more or less in danger from them, and not only in the hunger-months of the year. For belated wayfarers to be attacked and eaten by these fierce beasts was no uncommon thing.

So we find pitiful-hearted men, who nowadays would provide drinking troughs for horses and cattle, spending their money in erecting refuges on lonely parts of the road, to which travellers might fly when in danger from Wolves. Such a one was built at Flixton, near Filey, in the reign of Athelstan, there being then a terrible plague of Wolves in Yorkshire.

It was the tribute of money imposed by Athelstan on the Welsh king which was changed by his successor, Edgar the Peaceable, into a tax of 300 Wolf skins per annum. We learned this fact in our history books as little children, but what we were also taught as to the wonderful result, viz. that the country was thereby cleared of these four-footed pests—in less than four years, too— is most likely an exaggeration. No doubt, however, it did much to thin their numbers and scare them away to the lonelier parts of " Wild Wales."

We may be sure that the Sussex Wolves came down to feast on the bodies of Harold's brave Saxons as night closed in on the battlefield of Hastings ; indeed, one of the old Chronicles as good as tells us so. That must have been one of the terrors of a defeated army in those old days. But the watch-fires of brushwood soon

WOLVES.

set burning by the victors did something to keep the prowlers at a distance—

"The Wolf-scaring faggot that guarded the slain."

That great hunting-ground of the early Norman kings, the New Forest, must have sheltered many Wolves. In old records

HEAD OF WOLF.

[*Drawn by* COLBRON PEARSE.

we find mention of money paid to the Sheriff of Hampshire " for the livery (uniform) of the king's Wolf-hunters, falconers, etc."

At Carmarthen, in 1166, a mad Wolf bit two-and-twenty persons, nearly all of whom died. In King John's day, Devonshire still held many Wolves in its lovely valleys and wild moors. It is to that king's reign, too, that the sad story of Bedd Gelert belongs, which we all know so well. We may be pretty sure that

18

the legend which tells of the great Wolf killed by Llewelyn's favourite hound while guarding his master's infant son, and the misunderstanding which led the prince to stab the faithful creature, is founded on fact.　How we grieve for the dog !　How we feel for the prince !

> "Ah, what was then Llewelyn's pain? for now the truth was clear;
> The gallant hound the wolf had slain to save Llewelyn's heir."

In the days of Edward III. the monks of Wensleydale in Yorkshire were allowed by special order to take any of the deer or wild creatures of the forest which were found killed by Wolves ; but they were forbidden to guard their cattle by keeping mastiffs " to drive the Wolves from their pastures."　This was rather hard on the monks, but then the forest laws against killing any of the wild animals of the chase bore heavily on all who had to live where those animals were free to do mischief.

Sometimes the peasantry were encouraged to go out and kill the Wolves ; but usually they had to wait till the king or the lord of the manor chose to go a-hunting.　The season of the Wolf Hunt lasted from Christmas Day to Lady Day.

The last Wolf in England seems to have been killed in the reign of Henry VII.　But in Scotland, though every man's hand was against them, as sheep-stealers and cattle-slayers, it took two centuries more to hunt them down.　In James the First's reign a very desperate remedy was used—great tracts of woodland and thicket which were known to be the hiding-place of these animals were set on fire ; and the Wolves lurking in their dark depths either perished in the flames or were killed as they wandered about the surrounding country.

From that time onward stories of the "last Wolf" killed began to come in from different counties, but in the wilder parts of the Highlands they lingered for a long time.　Here is an exciting story of how one great she-Wolf was slain.

" She had made her den in a cairn or pile of loose rocks, whence she made excursions in every direction, until she became the terror of the countryside.　She killed several people, and, hearing of this, two young lairds resolved to destroy her.

" They set off alone from Strathglass, and having found out

her retreat they looked about for her. She was absent, but her cubs were lying in the den among the rocks, and one of the brothers drawing his dirk (dagger) crept in. While he was killing the cubs, the mother Wolf came bounding up. Mad with fury she sprang for the opening, taking no notice of the younger laird who

COMMON WOLF, AT THE ZOOLOGICAL GARDENS.

stood on guard there. He aimed at her with his hunting spear, but missed her and damaged his weapon.

"The elder brother not only had his dirk but also a steel gauntlet (glove) on his left hand. As the Wolf sprang at him, open-mouthed, he thrust his left hand into her jaws, and struck and struck with his dirk till, after a fierce struggle, the great beast fell dead."

The last Scottish Wolf seems to have been the one which was

killed in Morayshire, in the year 1743, by a doughty hunter named MacQueen, who slew the animal single-handed and brought its head to his chief. The brute had killed two children on the hills only the day before.

In Ireland Wolf-hunting was long kept up, the breed of dogs used being a tall rough-haired greyhound of great strength and swiftness. So useful and needful were these dogs that in Cromwell's day an " order in council " was made forbidding them to be sold out of the country. The last Wolf was killed in the Wicklow Mountains as late as 1770.

When once we cross the " narrow seas " we soon find ourselves in lands where—at all events in winter—the Wolf is still a pest and often a terror. The home of the European Wolf is away to the eastward—the dense pine forests of Russia, the rugged slopes and ravines of the Carpathian Mountains, and parts of Turkey and the Balkan States.

Napoleon's wars, of a hundred years ago, did much to encourage the Wolves and make them bold. His soldiers marched into many out-of-the-way places—the hills of Spain, the secluded mountain-valleys of Switzerland and the Tyrol, and the great lonely plains of Russia. And where there was fighting there was grim feasting—for the Wolves! Little cared they which side was victorious, so long as a plentiful supply of dead and wounded were left strewn about for them to devour.

Next to a defeated army they loved a hastily retreating one. For example, they are said to have hung on the flanks of the immense French host which invaded Russia in 1812. When it had to quit Moscow, owing to the city being set on fire, the homeward march began. It was a terrible time for the poor, tired, disappointed fellows : the cold was frightful, and thousands of them sank down in the snow, unable to go a step further. Some went forward, carried on the shoulders of kindly comrades ; others were left to die. The Cossacks came down upon them with their long spears, and the Wolves with their white teeth. The fierce brutes, " hunger-mad," flung themselves even on able-bodied soldiers, and tore them to pieces.

They did more. They followed the remnant of that army into Central Europe, and for years afterwards forests that had been almost free from Wolves were again infested with them.

Hunger will drive a Wolf any distance. Even nowadays an unusually severe winter sends packs of Russian and Austrian Wolves right across Europe even as far west as Belgium and Eastern France. Though, to be sure, France has her own native Wolves— in Brittany at least, where there is an official called Le Grand Louvetier, or, as we should say, Master of the Wolf Hounds.

The Lapps and the Norwegians who own flocks and herds of any kind—sheep, cattle, or reindeer—have often to do battle with the skulking thief. But better than aught else it loves the flesh of the horse. Many a one, with or without its rider, has had a great mouthful of solid flesh snapped out of its haunch by those fearful jaws before it could gallop out of reach.

But there are times when the tables are turned. Horses that live in a half-wild state on the open plains, and have not learned to look to man for protection, adopt a very clever plan for their own defence. As soon as the alarm has been given, the whole herd rushes together and forms a sort of ring, with the " babies " in the centre for safety's sake. So that the Wolves come racing up only to find a sort of quick-set hedge of thrust-out horse-heads, each with flashing eyes and yellow teeth that could break most of the bones in a Wolf's body.

The new-comers run round and round the herd, trying vainly to find an opening. None has been left. And they know that to try to force a way in between those heads and hoofs would mean certain death.

Nor are the horses content with merely defending themselves and their foals. Says Dr. Woods Hutchinson : " When all is in order, out trots the oldest horse, the war-lord of the herd, and paces proudly up and down in front of the line, looking for the enemy.

THE WOLF AND HIS PREY.

And woe betide the single Wolf that he can overtake before he can gain the shelter of the hills; his back will be broken by a sledge-hammer stroke of the front hoofs, and the life shaken out of him by the great yellow teeth, as if he had been a rat."

If a Wolf can take a reindeer herd by surprise he will often kill as many as thirty in a night. The little squat fellow who owns the herd takes the first opportunity to " hit back." Here is an account of a Lapp Wolf hunt.

" When Wolf tracks have been seen in the neighbourhood the swiftest runners on snow-shoes prepare for an exciting chase. The Wolf may have a start of a mile or two (for he is quick to take alarm), but the track he leaves in the deep snow is so clear that the hunters can follow it at top speed. On their snow-shoes they rush through the wood, glide down steep hills, and leap from ledges several yards high.

" Each hunter does his best to outrun the others, for the Wolf belongs to the Lapp who strikes the first blow. As soon as the leading hunter gets up close enough to the Wolf, he gives it a heavy blow across the loins with his stout spiked snow-staff. If other Wolves are on ahead, he kills it outright; if not, he disables it, and waits till the rest of the hunting-party come up, before despatching it."

A full-grown he-Wolf sometimes reaches astonishing length and strength. One of those kept at the Zoo, when it rose on its hind legs, as Wolves often do in their cages, stood six feet high. The head is always large, and the biting power of the long jaws is enormous.

Only a few years ago, in the month of January, a wedding party of peasants in Servia were returning from the town where the marriage had taken place. The night was so beautiful that they stopped the drivers of the sleighs, and got out to enjoy a walk over the firm hard snow. As they drew near the edge of a forest a pack of Wolves rushed out upon them, and not a single member of the company escaped. On the morrow a search-party found a few bones—all that remained of twelve persons.

Such incidents occur every winter, though not always with such dreadful results. A recent writer asserts that even in Russia very few travellers lose their lives nowadays through attacks by

Wolves, though sleighs are followed often enough. The travellers are nearly always armed, and shots can be fired in such quick succession from a modern rifle that even the boldest of the pack hesitate to come too near.

A winter or two ago a story reached the English newspapers, from Hungary, of a startling adventure which befell

THE AFGHAN WOLF.

a sturdy countryman who was being driven along a lonely forest-fringed road.

Just at the corner of the wood a Wolf dashed out after the sleigh and came pelting down the snowy road. The boy who was driving whipped up his horses in great alarm, and the countryman, remembering that he carried no firearms, grew anxious. On and on came the Wolf till it was abreast of the sleigh. Then, with a snarl, it leaped on the back of the man, who was crouching inside. Something prompted him to fling up his arms, and the next moment they had met over the rough neck of his fierce foe. Then he drew the brute down with all his strength and held it as if in a vice.

The horses seemed to know what had got into the sleigh, and simply flew along. The peasant held on to his enemy with all the might of his strong arms, though the beast kicked and struggled violently. At last the lights of the village twinkled in sight, and a few minutes later the man's neighbours came rushing out with sticks and pitchforks, and soon despatched the Wolf.

It was only with difficulty that the peasant could loose his grip on the animal, so stiff had his arms and wrists become with the tremendous strain of holding the Wolf pressed down.

It is said that any simple thing, such as a piece of rope, if trailed from the back of a sleigh, is enough to keep a Wolf-pack at a respectful distance. Like most persons with a guilty conscience, the Wolf is always suspicious, and until he is sure that the thing he fears cannot hurt him he will fight shy of it.

Hunters wishing to keep the body of some animal which they have killed free from the teeth of Wolves often succeed in doing so by simply tying a few fluttering strips of white paper or rag to the tops of sticks driven into the ground on either side of the body. And Mr. Theodore Wood mentions a case in which a certain district in Norway which used to be infested by Wolves was suddenly deserted by them ; the cause was traced to the putting up of telegraph posts and wires. The Wolves could not understand this ; they suspected danger, and—cleared out !

Possibly the shining steel of a railway line would scare them at first in the same way ; but they grow used to such mysterious things after a time, and come down and prowl beside the line.

Mr. Vaughan Cornish, when out on the prairies in Canada, in 1900, noticed how the Wolves had learned to know what times in the day the trains passed, and what was the most likely place for the train cooks to throw out the bones and scraps.

" In the grey cold dawn, the hungry coyotes, their tails tucked between their shaking legs, may be seen standing in the snow,

with their short ears pricked up like an anxious terrier's. . . .
Sometimes a great grey Wolf, the very picture of cold and famine,
is seen sitting by a sage bush, in the drift of snow powder raised
by the wind, his long sharp nose lifted in line with his spine, the
cutting blast ruffling up the fur on his back, waiting for the sun
to rise and warm him, and for the train to pass and leave him a
beef-bone to take off the edge of hunger."

The Coyote or Prairie Wolf is not a formidable animal, though

THE TASMANIAN WOLF.

[*Drawn by* JOSEPH WOLF.

to be beset by a pack is not pleasant. He is much smaller than
the ordinary Wolf, and the fur of the coat is longer. The timber
Wolves, on the other hand, are really strong beasts, and quite able
to give trouble.

An adventure with Wolves only a short distance from the
railway was reported from the south-east of Europe only the
other day.

A train was making its way through a snowy landscape, in

Moldavia, when the passengers saw, to their horror, two sturdy peasants fighting for dear life with a pack of Wolves. Happily the engine-driver saw them too, and the train was brought to a standstill. Instantly every man in it jumped out, and ran to the rescue. Some had revolvers, others had only sticks or sheath-knives, but so loud were the yells and shouts of the on-coming rescuers that the Wolves turned tail and fled. Help came only just in time ; a few moments more and the two poor fellows would have been torn to pieces. They were eagerly helped into the train, and were carried safely to the next station.

One curious fact has been noticed about a Wolf : fierce and persistent though the brute is in pursuing or attacking, the moment it finds itself trapped its spirit gives way. It shrinks and cowers, and shows itself utterly crushed. If it enters a house and finds the door of a room shut upon it, or if it tumbles into a pit and cannot scramble out, all its ferocity and strength seem to go from it, and it will often let its captor clutch hold of it and drag it out unresisting.

Wherever the Wolf is found—and he is to be met with in most countries of the world—he usually makes himself a nuisance. He is always more or less hungry, and when he sets out to get food for himself and his cubs, he plays the robber with much skill and daring.

So man's hand is against him. Different ways of hunting and trapping him are used in different countries. In Russia, nowadays, well-to-do sportsmen hunt him with hounds ; the latter are a very large and powerful species of white greyhound. Or he is taken in pitfalls and shot. Still another way is to drive in a sleigh through the forest, in time of hard frost when the Wolves are bold with hunger. At the back of the sleigh one or more sportsmen lie snugly under their fur rugs, with their rifles ready. A young pig is carried in the sleigh, and its cries soon reach the ears of the lurking Wolves, who cannot resist following the sleigh, and are speedily shot.

Perhaps the most picturesque way of hunting the Wolf is that which you may see in the west of Asia, on the bleak Kirghiz Steppes. The Tartar tribes are wonderful horsemen, and they ride after the Wolf in very large hunting parties. Not only are dogs used to overtake the quarry, but, because a fleet Wolf may get away from them, eagles are used. They are trained to help the hunter in very much the same manner as falcons were trained in the olden time.

The great bird sits on the hunter's wrist till it is time to be let loose. Then it soars into the air, sails after the Wolf, and swoops down upon it. Its duty is not to kill, but to "bother" the Wolf, by flapping its wings in its face and driving its sharp claws into the animal's back.

It makes capital sport for the riders, but, even apart from this, Wolf hunting is a real necessity in those parts, the brute being far too partial to the lambs and kids of the Tartars' flocks.

So dog-like is the Wolf in appearance that many attempts have been made to rear Wolf cubs as tame pets. So long as they remain cubs there is not much danger. The little creatures with their absurdly big heads and paws, and their grey-blue eyes are often charming, and seem to be really fond of their owners if kindly treated.

A German lady thus describes her experience with such pets : " My husband having purchased three young Wolves, we shut them up in a coop in the garden. Every morning, as soon as they heard me call out in the courtyard, ' Come, little fellows ! Come along, my little Wolves, and have your breakfasts ! ' they would answer my call as quickly as they could, all the while leaping and bounding with delight.

" After a month we gave away two of the cubs, but kept the third, and he made himself perfectly at home with the labourers on our farm ; but it was myself and my husband whom he followed in preference to any one else. In winter, when the charcoal-burners came, he would climb to the top of the wall, wag his tail, and keep on crying out to them till they came quite close up to him, and fondled him. He would sniff at their pockets to find out whether there was anything there to eat, and they would often bring him crusts of bread in their pockets.

" Our dog and the Wolf would eat out of the same wooden bowl, without there ever arising any dispute between them. We kept our Wolf a year, but his howls at night so disturbed our rest, that, at the end of that time, we were obliged to get rid of him."

As he grows up, a " tame " Wolf usually shows his Wolf nature, and can never be really trusted not to pounce or snap. But there have been cases—rare cases—where such Wolves, after being separated for many months from the person who used to feed and tend them, have shown the wildest joy at the sight of the friend whom they had missed.

A she-Wolf when angered is a terrible beast, but even she in her wild state does not always mete out death when she has the power and the chance. She has been known many a time to spare tiny children whom the father Wolf has seized and carried home to the den, and bring them up along with her own cubs. And when years after such children have been found and rescued, it has sometimes proved harder to teach them the ways and language of their brothers and sisters than they had found it to learn the ways and language of the Wolf cubs with whom they had been reared.

And so the delightful picture of Mr. Kipling's Mowgli, the little brown-skinned Indian boy, making himself at home in the she-Wolf's cave, and learning " the law of the jungle," and being admitted to the Seeonee Wolf-pack, has sober truth at the back of its romance.

THE END.

Printed by MORRISON & GIBB LIMITED, *Edinburgh.*

SUITABLE PRESENTATION BOOKS FOR BOYS.